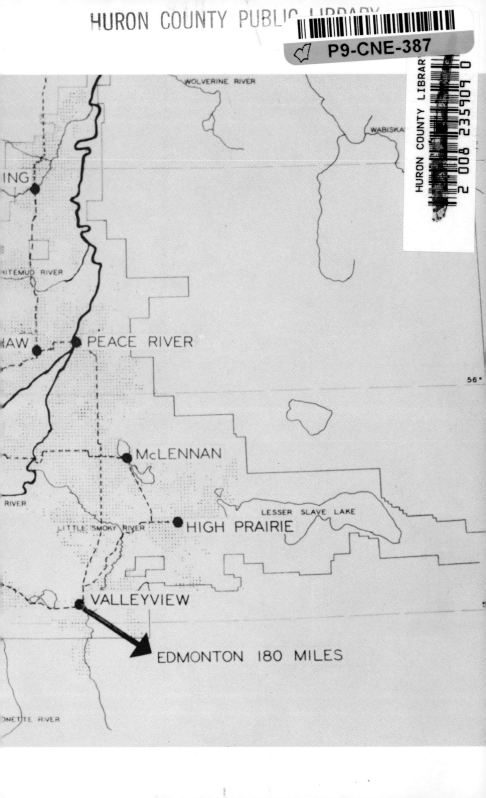

WOLVERINE RIVER

WABISKA

ING

WHITEMUD RIVER

56°

HAW   PEACE RIVER

McLENNAN

RIVER

LESSER SLAVE LAKE

LITTLE SMOKY RIVER   HIGH PRAIRIE

VALLEYVIEW

EDMONTON 180 MILES

ONETTE RIVER

Peace Country Heritage

Peace Country Heritage

by

E. C. Stacey

Western Producer Book Service
Saskatoon
1974

DEDICATED

To those, past and present, whose destiny it was, and is, to pioneer the development of a vast Inland Empire.

Copyright © 1974 by E. C. Stacey
Western Producer Book Service
Saskatoon, Saskatchewan
ISBN 0-919306-42-X

Printed and Bound in Canada by Modern Press

From this place which we quitted this morning the West side of the river displayed a succession of the most beautiful scenery I had ever beheld. The ground rises at intervals to a considerable height and stretches inwards to a considerable distance. At every interval or pause in the rise, there is a very gently ascending space or lawn which is alternate with abrupt precipices to the summit of the whole or at least as far as the eye could distinguish. This magnificent theatre of nature has all the decorations which the trees and animals of the country can afford it; the groves of poplar in every shape vary the scene; and their intervals are enlivened with vast herds of elk and buffaloes; the former choosing the steep uplands and the latter preferring the plains. At this time the buffaloes were attended with their young ones who were frisking about them and it appeared that the elks would soon exhibit the same enlivening circumstances. The whole country displayed an exuberant verdure; the trees that bear a blossom were advancing fast to that delightful appearance and the velvet rind of their branches reflecting the oblique rays of a rising or setting sun, added a splendid gaiety to the scene which no expressions of mine are qualified to describe.

Alexander Mackenzie's impressions of
Dunvegan, from his diary of May 10, 1793.

ACKNOWLEDGMENTS

The writer is greatly indebted to the late Dr. W. D. Albright, who recorded his thoughts and undertakings so meticulously and who filed a comprehensive story of the early settlement of the Peace River region. On his retirement his papers were forwarded to the Alberta Parliamentary Library and to the Glenbow Foundation, where they have been made freely accessible to the writer to supplement his own records. Published historical records and the personal recollections of many of Dr. Albright's contemporaries have been excellent reference material.

Particular reference is made to two comprehensive publications: *Peace River Chronicles,* by G. E. Bowes (Prescott Publishing Company), and *The Land of Twelve-Foot Davis,* by James G. MacGregor (Institute of Applied Arts Ltd.).

The writer has enjoyed the active co-operation of contemporary agrologists in assembling and interpreting their professional findings. The book is intended for the general reader and in no way is it a complete record of achievement or a scientific treatise. The fullest co-operation has been afforded by the writer's successor as Superintendent of the Beaverlodge Experimental Station, Dr. A. A. Guitard, and by Dr. L. P. S. Spangelo, his successor in turn, as Director of the Beaverlodge Research Station, Canada Department of Agriculture.

Much personal thanks is extended to my wife, Evelyn, and to Miss Isabel Campbell for editorial assistance.

ILLUSTRATIONS

Endpapers—*front:* Agricultural research in northwestern Canada

back: General grid of Peace River area

Photo Section I—*following page 50*

Threshing at Stoney Point, the Rutabaga Johnson farm, Beaverlodge, 1911.

Threshing outfit of the Beaverlodge Industrial Co. Ltd. moving to a new site.

Tour of the Beaverlodge plots by the United Farmers of Alberta, 1921.

The Charles McNaught and Dan Chambers families on the Edson Trail, 1912.

A mudhole on the Grouard Trail, 1913.

The metamorphosis of a hog house, the W. D. Albright residence, 1918, 1922, and 1940. Experimental Station, Beaverlodge.

Poster announcing a 1931 lecture by W. D. Albright.

More than 200 persons gathered for supper, the Albright lecture and a dance, sponsored by the North Pine Women's Institute, B.C.

The Illustration Station annual field day at Debolt, 1942.

Part of the group attending the Illustration Station field day at Fairview, 1933.

A group of students from Toronto and Montreal who in 1937 retraced the footsteps of the early explorers down the Parsnip and Peace rivers.

A group from Blueberry Mountain who came 100 miles in an open truck to visit the Beaverlodge Experimental Station, 1941.

The Sudeten settlers at Tomslake, B.C. on a field day at the Station, 1946.

Dr. and Mrs. G. Turesson, of Sweden, and Dr. L. E. Kirk, Ottawa, on the Athabasca ferry, 1934.

United States Vice-President Henry A. Wallace, Superintendent W. D. Albright, and Major David R. Nelson at the Grande Prairie Airport, 1944.

W. T. G. Wiener, Secretary of the Canadian Seed Growers' Association, with Mr. and Mrs. Herman Trelle at their home in the Lake Saskatoon district, 1933.

Ceremonial party at the unveiling of the Albright Cairn, Beaverlodge Experimental Station, 1954.
The plaque, Albright Cairn.

Photo Section II—*following page 146*

Field in the Halcourt district cut in two by severe erosion, 1935.
An out-apiary in the Hinton Trail district, 1964.
Alfalfa field at Clayhurst, B.C., 1939, which for several years
produced about 400 pounds of choice seed annually.
Sweet corn fodder shocked for livestock feed.
Gordon Moyer stooking his 110-bushel-per-acre oat crop in
the Elmworth district, 1928.
Picking saskatoon fruit in a selection row.
Seedling tomatoes from a breeding program at the Beaverlodge
Research Station.
Some 83 varieties or strains of apples or crabapples which bore
fruit at the Station, 1944.
Field peas, 1926.
Testing flax varieties, 1936.
Harvesting oat plots, 1926.
Haying test plots of alfalfa, 1935.
Harris Brothers of Beaverlodge picking up a swathed creeping
red fescue seed crop.
Bulk handling of creeping red fescue.
Machine-run creeping red fescue in storage awaiting processing.
Sacked creeping red fescue being loaded on a tandem truck
for transport to a central cleaning plant.
Creeping red fescue aftermath in late summer, awaiting late
fall or winter pasturing.
Midwinter pasturing on creeping red fescue.
William D. Clark in his vegetable garden at Thunder River,
N.W.T.
Rev. Father Adam, O.M.I. in his garden at Inuvik, N.W.T.
Jock Aitchison picking raspberries, Fort Vermilion Experimental
Station.
Dennis Collison's Toad River Ranch, Mile 422, Alaska Highway.
The Experimental Station at Mile 1019, Alaska Highway.
Beef cattle at the Experimental Station, Mile 1019, Alaska
Highway, after wintering in an open-faced shelter.

CONTENTS

PREFACE

What is the spirit of the Peace? Why is it different?

The Peace River region is a product of its isolation over the years, its ample resources of soil and water, its climate, and the spirit of its frontier.

This book is written in tribute to the many pioneers who settled in the Peace River region of northwest Alberta and northeast British Columbia and to greet those who will come to make their homes in this vast land and to the North beyond.

It portrays the spirit of the Peace, where there is much land to develop; where there are more opportunities than people to claim them; where highways are busy but uncrowded; where water and air are clean; where people live a richly satisfying life.

The book reflects problems of pioneering, the achievements of the people of the Peace within half a century, and the kind of people who made it all possible. It analyzes the settlement potential of Canada's Northwest and dispels some doubts which have been cast thereon.

It is a record of over half a century of agricultural research by a federal agency to probe the potentialities of a large block of semi-isolated land being settled by people of varying background. Historically, this is the period of the Beaverlodge Experimental Station and the transition to more intensive agricultural research by a Northern Research Group operating as a Research Station.

Few have been so fortunate as to enter a region so blessed with resources and to be given the opportunity to develop those resources to meet the insatiable demands of civilization. But it is the grave responsibility of society to create orderly development, and of the individual to pioneer with vision. Settlers of the Peace have been true to their trust; pitied at times for their sacrifices — needlessly so; in turn, pitying those who were not so fortunate as they were to have the opportunity to open a new region.

To the reader, the challenge is there. Within the next quarter century, developments within the region will be manifold. The resources are there — soil, timber, petroleum, coal, minerals, water power. You, the reader, may be amongst those still to come, but come in orderly fashion. Build as you penetrate. This has been the record of the Peace.

Rather than an account of the vicissitudes and struggles of pioneering, this is a record of dreams and achievements, determination and public service.

Essentially it is the story of one man, William Donald Albright, who met the challenge of the region in the name of his beloved Canada and who fought his way through discouragements and frustrations.

Associated with him were many — those who worked beside him, those for whom he worked, and those from whom he demanded much.

Reflecting his dedication to and deep love for the North and its people, Albright, pioneer and poet, wrote:

> Sing me a song of the open spaces,
> The broad white plains and the hardy races
> With buoyant hopes and with strong-set faces
> Peopling this Northern land.
>
> Sing me a song of her fertile acres,
> Whose breadstuffs gladden the world's best bakers;
> A tribute of praise to the brave home makers
> Holding the last frontier.
>
> Sing me a song of her mountain rivers,
> Whose cutbanks yawn where the aspen quivers.
> They rise in the hills where the avalanche shivers—
> Thousand league tides to the sea.
>
> Sing me a song of her vast resources,
> Of mines exposed where the river courses—
> Petroleum, coal and hydraulic forces,
> Gifts of the ages past.
>
> Sing me a song of the pluck and daring
> Of pioneers o'er the long trails faring.
> For their's is the breed that defies despairing—
> Shock troops of the North Frontier!

This was to have been Albright's book. He husbanded the material and cherished the responsibility — but Fate decreed otherwise. —E.C.S., 1973

Part I

Dr. William Donald Albright

1881-1946

PIONEER, JOURNALIST, HUMANIST

Superintendent, Dominion Experimental Sub-Station

1919-1945

Beaverlodge, Alberta

WESTWARD HO!

WILLIAM Donald Albright, enrolled in the Associate course at the Ontario Agricultural College at Guelph in 1901, was a timid lad who scarcely could face an audience. But he had determination and vision, as well as an avid interest in journalism and the effective use of language. Later in life he would ponder an hour or longer over the choice of a word to suit the text; if his editor stumbled even momentarily on sentence structure, he would insist that the sentence, though grammatically correct, be rewritten. Most of his staff found it taxing to meet the demands of a perfectionist.

It was inevitable that Donald Albright would drift into journalism. After graduation, he became editor of the *Maritime Farmer* at Sussex, New Brunswick. In 1905 he returned to Ontario as editor of the *Farmer's Advocate* at London, then a household organ to Ontario farmers.

Albright fared well in his new work until the federal election of 1911 when the issue of reciprocity with the United States was fiercely contested on all sides, and was favored by Editor Albright. However, editors do not have a clear mandate to voice their personal views. The advertisers, mainly from the farm machinery business, threatened to withdraw their support from the *Farmer's Advocate.*

What to do about Albright? His abilities were fully appreciated and the management of the *Farmer's Advocate* wished to retain his services. Fortunately, the publication maintained Weldwood Farm for practicing its precepts and for demonstration, so that its readers could observe developments in agricultural science as well as read about them. Albright was appointed manager.

About this time a mild hysteria hit staid Ontario and points east. Western Canada was opening up. Who could resist the opportunity to take part in the development of the vast hinterland, to acquire a new farm virtually for nothing, and to experience adventure? Much has been written about gold-rush fever. Easterners sold out and left for the West's land rush.

But where to go? The West was out there—"Can't you see it on the map?"

"How do we get there?"

"What do we live on until we become established?"

Historians have written about such groups as Selkirk's Settlers and the Barr Colonists. But most of the settlers in the early twentieth century came on their own. They did not attract the attention of the press.

Where to settle? The Portage Plains of Manitoba were good, but only just over the border from Ontario. The Regina Plains of Saskatchewan were also excellent, even though Palliser, a half century before, had gone to great lengths to report that the Triangle which now bears his name was unfit for farming.

Then there was the Peace River country of Alberta. It had to be good—it was very far away and very far north! What more could one ask?

Earlier in Canadian history when the route of the first transcontinental railway was to be chosen, an Ottawa lawyer, Malcolm McLeod, campaigned ardently in favor of the Peace River route. Son of a fur trader, he had been born in the Northwest Territories and knew the country. This sparked a survey by Charles Horetzky, a surveyor and naturalist who, with Professor John Macoun, botanist, visited the Peace in 1873. Horetzky was fully satisfied that a railroad could well be built through the country, while Macoun reported:

> From all observations I made, both in respect of soil and vegetation, I am satisfied that the whole country between Slave Lake and the Rocky Mountains is a continuation of the prairie. . . .
>
> Here, then, is a strip of country over 600 miles in length, and at least 100 miles in breadth, containing an area of 60,000 square miles, which has a climate no way inferior to that of Edmonton. I know that many doubts will be cast on the truthfulness of this statement but from a careful perusal of many published tables of the climatology of the district in question and my own observation, I can come to no other conclusion than this, that the day is not far distant when the most skeptical will believe even more

than I now assert. The summer frosts are due to radiation, and whether the settlement of the country will have any effect in lessening them, is a matter of speculation. It has always been so in Ontario, that summer frosts have ceased as the country became opened up. May this not be the case in Rupert's Land and the Peace River country?[1]

In 1903 the Geological Survey of Canada sent James M. Macoun to make a detailed survey of the Peace. Son of John Macoun, he could not agree with the earlier report:

After a perusal of all published reports on the Peace River country, examination of almost every acre of cultivated land in that region and a careful study of the natural vegetation, soil and climatic conditions, I have been forced to the conclusion that, notwithstanding the luxuriant growth that is to be seen almost everywhere, the Upper Peace River country will never be a country in which wheat can be grown successfully.

That this grain will mature occasionally there is no doubt, but that it will ever become the staple product of any considerable area I do not believe.

The fact must never be lost sight of that there have been very few attempts to grow grain except in the river valley and that when these attempts have been made, they have almost always failed. Without any exception, every report on the productiveness of the soil and the suitability of the climate for the growth of cereals refers to the river valley, not one of those who have stated that the whole Peace River region was suited to the growth of wheat having any other grounds for that belief than the evidence afforded by crops grown in the valley . . .

When it is remembered that the plateau from which so much has been expected is from 800 to 1,000 feet above the river and from 2,000 to 2,500 feet above the sea, it will be seen that as a general proposition it is a great deal to assume that at that altitude and in that latitude, there would be no severe summer frosts, even were there no evidence against that hypothesis. There is, however, abundant evidence that in many years there are severe frosts in June, July and August, frosts which, if they do not entirely destroy the growing crops, render wheat unfit for flour-making purposes . . .

I was told that 1903 was an exceptional year, but others, who reported the same conditions in other years, were told the same thing and there are enough of these 'excep-

[1] As reported in *Peace River Chronicles*, Gordon E. Bowes, ed. (Vancouver: Prescott Publishing Company, 1963), p 92.

tional' years to warrant the belief that they may be expected any time. Conclusions drawn from comparisons of mean temperatures, of hours of daylight, etc., are of no value when confronted with the undoubted fact that in one locality the thermometer falls to a point when wheat will be injured, while in another, it does not. It has been said and will be said, that with settlement the climate will change. Perhaps it will to a certain extent, but more is to be hoped for from hardier kinds of grain; grain that can adapt itself to severer conditions and which will ripen earlier. The Grande Prairie and Spirit River regions will undoubtedly be better suited for grain culture when they have been drained, so that water will not lie in the clay subsoil; but the simple cultivation of the soil can do little to ameliorate the climate . . .

While the country that has been described should, in the opinion of the writer, not be settled by either the rancher or the grower of wheat until there is more satisfactory evidence that it is suited for either of these pursuits, it may be safely prophesied that after railways have been built there will be only a very small part of it that will not afford homes for hardy, northern people who, never having had much, will be satisfied with little.

It is emphatically a poor man's country, a country where any hard-working man may, in a few years, gather around him a few head of stock — horses, cattle and hogs — where he will be able to grow vegetables and in most years barley and oats and sometimes even wheat. But it will be many years before anything can be grown for export, even with good transport facilities.

The building of the railway will lead to the development of the mines in northern British Columbia and these mines will afford a market for beef and pork at least; but until there is some such market, cash will be very scarce. During the construction of the Grand Trunk Pacific Railway, there of course will be a ready market for any produce grown near the route it will follow, but such a market cannot last more than a year or two and the demand for food products will cease when the road is completed.[2]

In the 1909 westward trek was a group of some fifty-one persons, members of the Christian Association, dissidents from the Free Methodist Church. They were interested in locating where ample land of good quality would promise a living and permit the group to maintain close contact with each other. They were en route to Redlow, in northern Alberta.

[2]*Ibid.*, pp. 212-213.

The Christian Association had outfitted in Edmonton with eighteen teams of oxen and became known as "The Bull Outfit," which seemed to be appropriate. Their route was by way of Athabasca and on to Lesser Slave Lake where a halt was made. The men of the party cut firewood for steamer passage down the length of Lesser Slave Lake for the women and the freight. The parties rejoined at Shaw's Point, thence to Grouard, Dunvegan, and "home," taking from April the twentieth to July the twelfth for the trip.

Their address was now Redlow, Alberta, in the valley of the Beaverlodge River, Peace River region. Some years before the arrival of the Christian Association, the settlers of the Beaverlodge River valley had elected to name their post office Redlow. The post office at nearby Lake Saskatoon was called Beaver Lodge. Later, the first post office in the district was renamed Lake Saskatoon and that of Redlow was changed to Beaverlodge.

Donald Albright, now married to Eva Lossing, decided to follow his wife's parents, the R. C. Lossings, members of the Christian Association. Traveling in style by horses and democrat, but not always in comfort, they arrived in 1913.

At Beaverlodge, the Albrights bought Mr. Lossing's South African scrip, a quarter section now part of the Federal Research Station. Another quarter section was homesteaded half a mile eastward. The Albrights had settled into pioneer life, in the Peace River region of Western Canada.

SETTLING IN

EARLY settlement in the Grande Prairie area was centered at Lake Saskatoon and at Flying Shot Lake.

"Prairie" in a parkland region carries a different connotation from "prairie" in the Palliser Triangle. The story goes that in 1887 Bishop Grouard was camped at Flying Shot Lake and ran short of grub. This necessitated a trip to Lake Saskatoon fifteen miles away to shoot ducks. There his campfire got away and burned the tree growth from a large area, as far as Pouce Coupe and across the Smoky River. The following year a similar circumstance happened to Allie Brick at Shaftesbury Settlement near Peace River Landing. Thus, because of fire, small grassy areas were found by the early settlers before the forest could regain its cover; hence Grande Prairie, High Prairie, Salt Prairie, and a host more. Sunset Prairie was the name given to a mere twenty acres of grassland. Regardless of its size, a patch of grassland meant crop land without the labor of felling trees and grubbing roots. The stage was set for the Bull Outfit in 1909 and for W. D. Albright in 1913.

The pioneers were well pleased with their prospects. The soil was easily worked and highly productive. Meadows were knee-deep in luscious grass and peavine. Unfortunately a large proportion of arable land was classified Gray Wooded soil which, if it is not understood, is indeed a problem soil; some circles in Edmonton and elsewhere still discount the Peace as second-rate because of its wooded soil. Even locally, this erroneous concept has had to be corrected. As late as 1936 newcomers from the drought-ridden, bankrupt prairie lands of Saskatchewan were greeted with the chilling advice that they were too late — the good soil had all been taken up. Since then, hundreds of thousands of acres of bush land have been broken annually and the rate is increasing. Value implies ability to cope with problems. It is significant that the Peace country is still being settled and settlement will continue for many years.

Settlement in the Peace was indeed a reality even before the postwar rush of 1918, to the point that it attracted government interest. There have been various governmental policies to aid landseekers to secure and develop holdings. Some of them have been good.

The infamous "Cow Bill" was not. The settlers needed cattle and readily obtained ample loans for purchases. Unfortunately the cattle supply was limited. Bidding went high — twice economic value. But who would be a piker in such times? The money was spent and the livestock found new homes.

Then came the winter of 1919-1920, the longest on record. Feed supplies were low. Remaining cash reserves were spent on feed at increasing cost until funds or feed ran out. Cattle, still to be paid for, died or were shot. In the Halcourt district the barn of the late Russell Walker is evidence of the trade by a neighbor of roofing lumber for straw cover of very questionable quality in a vain effort to keep his cattle alive until spring.

Is it any wonder many farms were deserted for years afterward while their owners "worked out"? Later, during the depression years of the thirties, these same farmers faced disastrous commodity prices and heavy freight rates. The grim saying was that since the market price of a steer in Edmonton wouldn't pay the price of the freight bill, the solution was to ship an extra beast — by freight, of course!

There was a brilliant lesson in economics at this time. In faraway Pouce Coupe and Rolla, some 500 teams hauled produce 70 miles over the winter road to Spirit River elevators and a few farmers used the 120-mile summer road to Grande Prairie. Chartered banks and other credit-issuing services ruled the district uneconomic and refused to make loans for cattle. At first, this seemed a bitter hardship, but a few years later when others were still paying for a cow which had cost $250, plus accumulated interest — with cattle selling at $50 — the people of the Pouce Coupe and the Rolla districts seemed well off.

Sunset Prairie and Fort St. John were settled under the Soldier Settlement Act, which proved generally beneficial elsewhere. Here, though, homesteaders were located up to 80 miles beyond Pouce Coupe by dirt roads slashed through the bush and with two very deep river valleys to traverse. In their isolation they were all but forgotten, except for the annual collection visit which officials came to regard as hazardous to personal safety. It was a common sight in midsummer about 1924 to meet a string of "four-ups" with two wagons each, en route 120 miles or more to Grande Prairie — driven by women who, with their children, slept beneath their wagons and doubled up their teams on the hills — to market loads at prices which would barely return cost of production to farmers living under the shadow of the grain elevators.

The sight would have made yardage for a Canadian Broadcasting Corporation documentary.

Also, the region experienced the "Wanham Project" after World War II. A munificent Department of Lands and Forests set out to pay homage to war veterans by having them draw lots out of a hat for ready-made farms without buildings, fences, or livestock. It was fortunate that many worthy veterans were already settled under better programs; it was unfortunate that most of those who applied for the Wanham Project land were virtually unfamiliar with the practices of northern agriculture, which are quite different from those of the wheat-growing Prairies. It was even more unfortunate that the land was broken under construction contract principles which demanded very deep plowing — as much as eighteen inches — to cover roots, stumps, and even logs. The result was that the fields were mantled with sterile cellar clay.

The veterans struggled, the government came to their rescue ad infinitum, until finally the initial block of land was converted into a community grazing lease. The lease prospered under proper management. As the breaking progressed mistakes were corrected and the settlers fared better.

Sons of neighboring Ukrainian farmers would have been pleased to file on the Wanham land without government aid. In a few years they would have made it into a flourishing settlement.

HOMESTEADING

THE Albrights settled down to homesteading. Donald hauled logs and broke land. Mrs. Albright assisted her father in the new post office.

Albright found the work strangely frustrating in its inexactness and uncertainties. His editorial work on Ontario's agricultural problems had sharpened his appreciation for scientific farming. Now he and his neighbors were sowing wheat and oats — but what were the varieties and were they adaptable? Some were satisfied if the seed was sound; if the crop ripened late they attributed their misfortune to bad luck. But Albright wasn't satisfied. He was confronted with too many questions which he could not answer. Marquis wheat was new; would it be adaptable? Would grasses and clovers grow? Would vegetables and small fruits succeed?

In 1912 S. J. Webb, of the nearby Lake Saskatoon district, had been commissioned by Dr. J. H. Grisdale, Director of Dominion Experimental Farms, Ottawa, to conduct a few simple tests. After Webb left the area, Albright wrote Dr. Grisdale, offering to make some tests if the seed was furnished. The seed was supplied, and in 1914 Albright sowed half a dozen plots of grain on his South African scrip SE-1-72-10-W6 with a 20-run grain drill powered by four oxen. Some vegetable seeds and a few rows of alfalfa were sown by hand.

Herman Trelle, a Lake Saskatoon district farmer who was later to attract the attention of the agricultural world to the Peace River region through his many award-winning samples, visited those first plots and afterwards recalled that his interest in improved grain dated from that inspection.

Acknowledging Albright's report, Dr. Grisdale remarked that it showed promise. He proposed to institute an Experimental

Sub-Station[1] and offered the experimentalist $200 to repeat his tests the next year.

In 1915 the work was again conducted and ripe pumpkins were among the achievements. Grain plots were cradled that year. In 1916 the remuneration was raised to $400 and plots were planted on freshly broken land. A windbreak and some small fruits were planted in a half-acre plot west of the Albright house.

In 1917 the work was repeated. In June Dr. Grisdale wrote that he expected immigration after the war, with many questions arising for which the Dominion Department of Agriculture should be prepared. Accordingly, he proposed to lease twenty acres of land and pay the manager a part-time salary. After a month's hesitation Albright accepted this offer and purchased an additional twenty-five acres of Lossing land to enlarge his holdings. Mr. Paul Flint, a member of the 1909 Bull Outfit, was employed as Albright's assistant, having special charge of horticultural work, acting as general plotman, and helping to clear land.

That July, Albright met Dr. Grisdale at the Lacombe Experimental Station and plans were developed for systematic testing of grains and meadow crops. The latter were featured from the start because they presented a larger question mark than cereals and were considered essential to permanent agriculture.

Starting April 1, 1919, Albright became Superintendent of the Experimental Sub-Station at Beaverlodge. Testing was to be undertaken on forty acres of his land, for which he would receive an annual rental of $10 per acre plus $75 per year for horse hire. The lessor reserved the right to use the implement shed situated on the premises for his personal use as well as for experimental purposes. This rental agreement, with minor amendments, remained in force until the entire farm of about 318 acres was purchased in 1940 by the Dominion Department of Agriculture. The purchase was long overdue but money was scarce in the depression years. In 1941 the nominal status was changed from that of Sub-Station to Station. (See Appendix I.)

---

[1]This was the common spelling in the early years; later the form became "Substation."

Working conditions at the Beaverlodge Sub-Station were crude at the start. The open-front shed, where crops were threshed and samples prepared, gave way to a barn-like structure in 1920 but the straw-roofed horse barn remained until 1934. Other buildings were sadly needed as the tempo of work quickened. Periodically, senior officials from the Central Experimental Farm at Ottawa braved the long train trip from Edmonton to see the region firsthand. Director E. S. Archibald made a brief visit in 1920 but did not see this unit of his command again until 1944.

Albright was community-minded. When the Prohibition issue was rampant, he offered to take on all comers who favored the Evil. Fighting Joe Clarke, lawyer and erstwhile mayor of Edmonton, took up the challenge. The duel was one-sided; the brilliant lawyer was somewhat of an orator and the timid Albright was only emerging as a verbal protagonist of causes.

But the Albright pen was never daunted. He wrote articles on the Coast Outlet, the economic development of resources, and the "Sunshine Trail Through the Peace" and had them published in prominent newspapers, *Maclean's Magazine* and the *Canadian Geographical Journal.* His weekly column in local papers was a mixture of farm news, weather notes, sonnets, and Elbert Hubbard maxims.

There was but one District Agriculturist to serve the Alberta section of the Peace River region. Occasionally officials from Victoria, with varying credentials, traveled into the settled areas beyond the Alberta border and for many years provided a kind of service by carrying such messages from Sunset Prairie to Rolla as that the bull "Joe" had bought as a calf could now be picked up.

Albright's early reluctance to face an audience vanished. His favorite locale became the country schoolhouse, sometimes two meetings a day for several days, driving by team until as A. E. Ottewell, founder of Alberta University Extension Service, would say, "Eventually I arrived home and they poured me into bed."

"A Dozen Lectures Offered by the Beaverlodge Sub-Station," his prepared mimeographed informational brochure announced, would be mailed to any group's program committee looking for a speaker. On a take-your-pick basis, his topics were presented for selection:

Not by Bread Alone. 145 slides; time, 2 hours or more. Not a sermon but a racy lecture on horticulture, home-making and citizenship interspersed with sing-songs from words thrown on the screen. Fun and information for young and old. Bring the children.

Horticulture At Beaverlodge and Morden. Twenty-odd slides from Morden Experimental Station with any desired number of Beaverlodge slides; 1 hour or more. Talks on potatoes, vegetables, fruits, shelter-belts, ornamentals or any special aspects of horticulture. Young and old invited.

To The Arctic By Air. 70 slides, mostly from photographs taken by the author in July 1930; 2½ hours.

Homestead Days. 30 to 40 slides, 1 to 2 hours. An enter-taining, illustrated account of pioneer experiences of the Superintendent and others, commencing with trail days but emphasizing chiefly such practical matters as getting estab-lished on the homestead; logging; building; clearing and breaking; providing a water supply; keeping frost out of cellars; fuel supply; financing on little or nothing, etc. Espe-cially suitable for pioneer neighbourhoods. A smile, a laugh, a word of sympathy and some helpful suggestions.

Vancouver Harbour. Two dozen slides, ½ hour. Little discussion or comment.

Hard Times. "Nature, causes and how to meet them." No slides. 1 hour. A discussion of the causes and occurrence of the alternating spasms of good and hard times; prob-abilities of their recurrence; hints from experience on how to guard oneself against the depressions when they recur and how to meet them when here.
"Do not fail," urged a woman auditor in 1932, "to give this talk wherever you go."

Field Husbandry. 30 Beaverlodge slides; 1 hour or more. Land clearing; breaking; ploughing; harvesting methods; snow-water utilization; crop rotation, etc.

Cereals. 30 Beaverlodge and other local slides; 1 hour or more. Varieties; culture; registration; handling of pure seed blocks, etc.

Forage Crops. 30 Beaverlodge slides; 1 hour or more. Meadow crops; inoculation of legumes; annual forage crops, etc. An important subject in all established regions.

Live Stock — Management. 35 slides, 1 hour or more. Featuring chiefly cattle, hog and poultry experience and experiments at Beaverlodge.

Live Stock — Breeds and Types. 60 slides, 1 hour. A pleasing series of pictures supplied by the Ontario Department of Agriculture, depicting the leading breeds of horses, cattle, sheep and swine; also parts of the horse, cuts of butcher stock, etc.

Other subjects of limited call include a demonstration (with sieves and samples) on preparing grain for exhibition; talks on handling fall fairs, judging competitions and field days; to make the most of them; planning the farm business, etc. etc.

If in the foregoing list one does not see the subjects he wants, let him ask for it so long as it pertains to agriculture, horticulture or rural life.

To any accessible point in northern Alberta or northern British Columbia, the services of the Beaverlodge staff are available on two conditions: viz., that a hall be provided without expense to the Experimental Station and that some responsible organization, individual or group of citizens guarantee to have it heated, lighted and opened to permit commencement **exactly** at the appointed hour.

During the depression years he responded readily to invitations to lecture to farm groups. Their lot was hard, and invariably they received inspiration which would make the load lighter. As an amateur economist he predicted better times in the offing and paraphrased a popular song of the period:

> *Busy days will come again:*
> *The world will want our wheat again;*
> *When Commerce finds its feet again.*
> *Better times will come again.*

Naturally, Albright experienced many unusual circumstances incidental to delivering these lectures. One night he checked into the hotel at Brownvale and being a stickler for propriety, searched the unmanned desk until he found the register and recorded his stay below the last notation: "Loftus Goodall, Seed Branch, Calgary, August 21." Now it was May the second, nine months later. In nearby Berwyn Hotel the night clerk would obligingly leave a note on his desk when he retired about midnight. This listed the vacant rooms. The late traveler would scratch one from the list and report to the desk clerk next morning. If there was no list the weary traveler would look into rooms, doors open or closed, until he found an empty bed.

Robert Watson, as clerk of the Beaverlodge Sub-Station, recalled driving Albright in midwinter to a meeting in the Big Horn schoolhouse north of Lake Saskatoon. The snowdrifts were three feet deep in places and the team was near exhaustion when their destination was reached. They were twenty minutes late. The speaker was apologetic for breaking his own rule of strict punctuality.

At a meeting in the Gundy schoolhouse Albright was in fine form, urging settlers to husband their soil and live well. The lunch was nicely served and the lecture was to continue until at least midnight. It was a good opportunity to meet the audience and to instill a little more enthusiasm into the district.

"You have a fine district here and you will live well," Albright commented.

"Ye-es, as long as the relief checks keep coming!"

He loved the hardy Norwegian settlers and was overjoyed with an invitation to lecture at Valhalla Centre, but as he approached the hall a little old lady stopped him. "Mister, do you buy hides?" Momentarily Albright slid off Cloud Nine, taken aback at this blow to his prestige.

Albright's philosophical mind could not visualize Canada as a thin line stretching 3,000 miles from the Atlantic to the Pacific. To become really great, Canada must extend northward! Today he would be happy with the Roads to Resources, the Dew Line and the Arctic Oil Play. He coined the slogan "The Future of Canada Lies in Its Breadth" and used it on every occasion which provided an opening.

★ ★ ★

William Donald Albright was born in South Cayuga, Haldimand County, Ontario, in 1881 of Josiah D. and Sarah Elizabeth (Moyer) Albright. The family moved to Beamsville when Donald was thirteen years old, to a fruit farm. Donald attended high school for two years, followed in 1901-3 by a two-winter course at the Ontario Agricultural College, where he won the Governor-General's prize for general proficiency. Mrs. Albright was the former Eva Belle Lossing, of Otterville, Ontario, daughter of Robert C. Lossing. Grandfather Albright, who settled in Haldimand County on his arrival in Canada, had a remarkable library of books on science, travel, exploration, education, and religion. It was one of these books which first engaged Donald's interest in Canada's hinterland. For a while his interest fluctuated between Ontario and the West. He rebelled at the "Little Canada" idea and realized that Canada could be great only by pushing back her northern frontier.

Donald Albright was ably supported by his wife, Eva. In the early years of the Sub-Station she assisted in compiling production records and in other office routines. Their daughter, Eileen (Mrs. William Ross), now resides in White Rock. The elder son, Bruce, served in World War II as an R.C.A.F. pilot and was killed in action over Essen. The younger son, Gordon, is a social service worker in Edmonton.

ALBRIGHT THE CITIZEN

W ILLIAM Donald Albright cherished one ideal: to make Canadians aware of their heritage and their responsibilities.

It can be said that he cared more about how people lived and thought than about professional agriculture. Why else would he spend countless hours in country schoolhouses advocating better living, exemplified by neat woodpiles and a rocking chair on the veranda?

He also sent out thousands of packets of strawberry stolons and raspberry roots to aid new settlers in their homemaking.

About 1920 Albright wrote the pamphlet "Grande Prairie Capabilities" for the benefit of incoming settlers. But in 1921 homesteaders' enthusiasm was low; many prepared to give up. Albright rallied hope with the treatise "In the Trough of the Wave," indicating that pendulums do swing and times would be better:

> Throughout the Peace River Country of late there has been a prevalent spirit of depression. What is the cause? General hard times? Transportation? The dry season? All these enter in, but there is a greater factor than any of them. Inflation of hopes and values, with its resultant reaction, is the tap root of our present difficulty. It has manifested itself in many ways — land prices for example.
>
> Nine years ago the writer bought raw land on the Grande Prairie for $12.50 per acre, this being rather below than above the current asking price. Five dollars would have been plenty if common sense rather than inflation had been the gauge. When the early settlers came into the North Country some of them were expecting the locomotives to scorch their heels. From as far south as Texas they hurried to Pouce Coupe to get in ahead of the railway. Rosy immigration propaganda, townsite speculation and extensive wheat farming have been forms in which inflation has expressed itself.
>
> Interest rates are another evidence. An eastern farmer would be staggered at the nonchalance with which struggling

settlers borrowed money at twelve per cent in the early days, while more recently they borrowed all they could at nine. It does not necessarily follow that the banks are charging too much. They took unusual risks. The point is that farmers freely hired money on these terms. If a business earns three per cent and the proprietor borrows capital at nine, compounded every three or four months, the cream is soon skimmed off his earnings.

The majority of settlers take too long chances in cropping, raising wheat where they should grow oats, and oats on land where hay or pasture is the only safe crop.

No less fatuous was the general investment in live stock at the abnormal prices prevailing two or three years ago. Men bought cattle then who have since been unable to realize for the stock plus its natural increase, the half of what they paid for it with borrowed funds. This might be called "making money backwards."

The history of the West is replete with instances of whole districts becoming so hard-pressed and discouraged that nearly all who could pull up stakes and move away, did so. A few stuck, from necessity or dogged determination. Then the tide turned, setting them on their feet and eventually they became well off, while those who left, not a few kept on shifting and seldom amounted to very much.

The Peace River Country is naturally one of the choicest agricultural regions that lies out of doors. Picturesque and fertile, with long easy slopes, well drained yet well adapted to cultivation, it is capable of being developed — indeed is already in some instances being developed — into a land of fine farms and happy homes. The main thing needed is the more general inspiration of a true ideal. Without this, cheapened transportation would be likely, by fostering grain raising for export, to contribute to despoliation as it has done on vast areas of the lower plains. If the present hard times have the effect of getting more of us started on the path of mixed farming, with correlated attention to home making and citizenship, they will in the end prove a blessing, hard as the experience may be for individuals during the transition period. These deserve every consideration and sympathy. They should be given a chance to co-operate in improving their condition. They have not been without plenty of temptation to imprudence. The banks, the business men, the Soldier Settlement Board, the Departments of Agriculture, all share the responsibility with the man on the land for the state of affairs that has come to pass. There is no party left to throw stones. And yet, since all have acted for the best, there is no chance for recrimination. It is simply a case of getting our bearings and steering a wiser course in the future.

The idea that a man must change his location in order to succeed is one of humanity's persistent illusions. He who runs away from a failure without grasping the cause of that failure is only inviting a repetition somewhere else.

The effect was inspirational. Settlers took heart. Life seemed worth living. There have been depressions since, but each generation must learn its lessons anew. Hardships of homesteading remained in Albright's memory and generously infiltrated his writings. He admired Amos Sherk's philosophy — "Spend this year what you made last year."

To incoming settlers his advice invariably was "Put half of your money in the bank and do not touch it for five years. If you have been successful, you can well use it then. If you have been unsuccessful, you will need it."

In 1925 Albright penned his reaction to the North:

When, after twelve years residence on the frontier, I read lurid tales of Northern adventure, distorting geography for purposes of disguise, composing characters to avoid personal revelation and embellishing with misguided imagination where knowledge falls short, I think to myself how much more interesting the simple truth would have been. There is a mine of human interest in the story of the Canadian frontier. All that it needs is to be interestingly told. Too often the interest of biography is dulled by prosaic recital; the dramatic denouement is lacking. Preserve this, as Carlyle did in his *History of the French Revolution* and what novel can compare in gripping interest? Truth may or may not be stranger than fiction but to many it is more satisfying.

For some years the writer has been piecing together the story of the Peace River Settlement. Far back it leads. In the eighteenth century white men trod the Northern wilderness and left their impress.

From the corners of the earth they have come — from all the older provinces of Canada and many states of the Union; from Australia, Honolulu, South Africa; from Britain, Iceland, Finland, Sweden, Denmark, Russia, Germany, Holland, France — yes, even from Japan, home of Wada the famous 'Musher.' Americans, such as Peter Pond, have often been among the more daring pathfinders, though perhaps the largest permanent impress has been made by Scotchmen and Eastern Canadians. In the blend of blood with the native races the predominant elements are Scotch and French.

In the life stories of these men and women are the warp and woof of Northern development.

Traders and trappers, explorers and argonauts — backwash of the Cariboo and the Klondike rushes — policemen, prospectors, surveyors, navigators, naturalists, missionaries, teachers, ranchers, homesteaders, farmers, railroaders, capitalists with ever and anon a sprinkling of the world's flotsam that wastes itself among the aborigines in far away places; diverse as they are, they have nearly all been people of marked individuality, eccentric or unbalanced sometimes but possessing positive outstanding characteristics. The timid have stayed behind.

> 'Send not your weak and your feeble,
> Send me your strong and your sane.'

Touched here and there by the highlights of hairbreadth adventure; rich in the grim humor of incident, scintillating with sometimes tragic romance, the lives of the prominent trail makers have been distinctively characterized by courage, resourcefulness and fortitude. Indomitable is the keynote adjective of their makeup.

Nearly all are ordinary men in dress, manner and action. Only in the underlying traits of character do they excel. These traits are revealed in what they do, what they endure and how they bear themselves. Unheroic in manner, they are real heroes in the fibre of their beings — shock troops of the North Frontier.

The individual human looms large in thinly populated places. In cities he may be lost in the mass. In the wilderness he stands clean-cut in silhouette, the man known for what he is. 'Moccasin telegraph' is far and fast.

In 1913 enroute to the Peace River Country, I fancied myself something of a pioneer. Four hundred and fifty miles beyond steel seemed a fair distance from town. Vain ego! I was to realize that the trails we were to tread, faint though they seemed from Ontario, were long-beaten ones which hundreds of feet besides the Indians' had been treading through bush and plain.

But not until reaching Fort Vermilion on the Lower Peace in 1924 did I fully realize how late a comer I had been. There on the banks of the broad-bosomed river, six hundred and fifty miles north of the International boundary, I stood as one entranced, recalling a few from a long list of notable figures who had passed that way from the days of Mackenzie down to the time of Bishop Bompas, Lord Rhondda, Warburton Pike, Ernest Thompson Seton, Agnes Deans

Cameron, Emerson Hough and Hudson's Bay officials without number. Few places of its size stand out so prominently in geography and history. On the brink of the river bank stood, grim and silent, a Hudson's Bay Company flour mill. On the bank beside it, an old 'Peace River' steamboat lay dismantled and rotting, succeeded by a new and splendid one, the 'D. A. Thomas' which had brought us down. And yet Fort Vermilion is not the North. It is merely a portal to the North. Beyond is the Slave River, Great Slave Lake, and the mighty Mackenzie draining the region of an empire yet to be.

In March, 1937, Journalist Albright was called to headquarters at Ottawa. It was time to publish the chronicle "Fifty Years of Progress on Dominion Experimental Farms 1886 - 1936" and Albright was to be its editor, a deserving compliment. The task took a month to complete. Tales are told that he trod on many departmental toes in the need for haste, something that officialdom seemed to avoid, being conditioned to a more leisurely pace. Carl Fraser of the Cereal Division was thought to be spokesman for a group of superiors when he ventured the suggestion that as Albright was now firmly attached to an editing position at Ottawa, he might well remain thus. The explosive response caused the Director's office to tremble. Albright started to pack.

Anyway, he was anxious to be back in the Peace to see the crop.

In the summer of 1939, refugees from Sudetenland in Czechoslovakia migrated to Tupper Creek in the heart of the Peace River region. Of the 152 families and 37 single men, a total of 518 souls, most were tradesmen, office workers, and professional men, fewer than 5 per cent with farming experience.

Establishment of these people on farm lands, comprising the Sudeten Settlement, was placed under the supervision of the Canada Colonization of the Canadian Pacific Railway.

Albright was invited to address the Sudeten colonists in 1941:

> I have tried to imagine myself suddenly wrenched from my home by war, succoured by an ally, thrown among strangers although hospitable people, speaking a different language, then being transplanted five or six thousand miles to a pioneer region, obliged to learn a new occupation in which everything was strange, then before getting really

on my feet to run into a season such as this, with a good crop in prospect but with 57 rainy days out of 83 from July 20 to October 11—I need not picture the rest. You know it only too well. It must be very trying indeed.

In such a case the experience of the past is helpful. We read the future by the past. I have lived almost 28 years in the Peace. I have been through the mill myself and have learned some 'wrinkles' as we say. If I can pass them along to you, or if in any way at any time our Station can be of service to you, it will be a very great pleasure indeed. It is a pleasure as well as a duty to serve. Please regard us as your friends.

Pioneering nearly always spells privation. The world over, it is the price exacted by Nature for the privilege of virgin opportunity. It has been the case with the settlement of practically all new regions. Sometimes the privation takes one form, sometimes another, but always there are tests of courage and fortitude. They vary from region to region but they have hardship in common. There is nothing like perspective.

The Beaverlodge settlers, like other early arrivals, travelled via Lesser Slave Lake, Peace River, Dunvegan, Spirit River and Grande Prairie — 550 miles to Beaverlodge.

No homes awaited them. The land was unsurveyed. They squatted on approximate locations figured out by driving a wagon over the land and counting the revolutions of the wheel. They tented until they could throw up log shacks. Some lived under canvas until December in below zero weather. In these the men, women and children were healthier than they were later in warm homes. There were no doctors and they hadn't time to be sick. They went to town, as they did once a year in winter; it was at first a 900 mile trip — 450 out and 450 back. They learned to think and provide ahead. Dried fruit was the only kind purchased. Berries and game were obtained locally.

In the early days most of the crop was stacked and as threshing outfits were few it was not uncommon for steam outfits to be trundled about scrunching through deep snow, into December or even January. Often the snow had to be shovelled off the stacks before operations commenced.

In 28 years in the Peace I have seen 28 kinds of seasons, for the only regular feature of the climate is its irregularity. I have seen seeding commence as early as March and again as late as the middle of May. I have seen winter set in to stay once as early as October 20. Again I have seen ploughing on the last day of November and roses blooming at the beginning of that month. Many a time the situation has been discouraging, but always we have pulled through, though sometimes in looking back we wondered how we did it.

One of the commonest troubles has been a tantalizing interruption by rain or snow at threshing time. Seldom have we escaped it, though never in my experience has there been quite such a trying and prolonged period of wet weather as in 1941. Always before we have been able to get the threshing done and in only two or three cases has it been necessary to thresh grain in a tough condition.

After reviewing in detail the seasons, Albright gave the following advice, which has been preserved in written form:

One thing I have noticed through 28 years of pioneering experience. It is this: That he who improves his opportunities always has a chance to sow and reap. The laggard may get caught and we all may have our misfortunes, but there is generally a chance to harvest and to thresh, however belated it may be.

The most valuable lessons are learned in adversity. Opportunity comes to those who wait. Do not get panicky and work to no purpose.

Prepare for the worst and be ready for the best. This is not a bad climate on the whole but it can be cruel to the unprepared.

Play safe with early varieties and with methods that tend to safe maturity. Early seeding does not invariably give the largest crop but it is safest and gives the best average yields of grain.

Raise a variety of things. Don't put all the eggs in one basket.

Keep close' to a self-supporting basis, producing on the farm as much as possible of what the livestock and the family require. There may not always be a demand for what we wish to sell, but there is always a market for what we can eat and use. Never fail to plant and care for a good garden.

Keep livestock but not too much. Better to sell the surplus in a year of abundance — still better to carry it over — than to have to buy on a famine market.

Build up and hold reserves of seed, feed and cash. Follow Joseph. For many years I have always carried over a year's supply of seed grain and nearly a full year's supply of feed. Stack the good clean straw and hold it over against emergency.

Mixed farming steadies the flow of income, modifying the

peaks and dips due to price fluctuation. In the autumn of 1923 oats were hardly worth the cost of threshing. One farmer shipped a carload out and got a bill for part of the freight. I held my oats over for feed. The next year was droughty and oats were a good price. I eventually marketed my 1923 crop through pigs at 13 cents a pound live weight.

Keep a good woodpile ahead against bad weather or sickness.

Be thorough in everything. Whether erecting a building, setting up a stook, building a stack or caring for a team or piece of machinery, take pains. Oil is cheaper than castings.

As soon as possible get together and keep a nest egg of cash. In farming and especially in a new country, thrift is the secret of success. It is always easy to spend a dollar — not nearly as easy to get it back. Bargains come to the man with cash in hand.

Farm for the future. Keep the land clean. Keep it from washing and drifting. Do not break up draws where running water may cut out gullies. Top soil is precious. Take care of it. Husband the land — don't mine it.

During the depression of the 1930's Albright was deeply concerned. People must do something about conditions. Everyone must act. Being a man of action he wrote a letter to the press, proposing a 10 per cent reduction in salaries across the board.

The next week he was returning on the Edmonton, Dunvegan and British Columbia Railway from Pouce Coupe when a burly trainman accosted him.

"Are you Albright?"

Albright came close to being thrown off. His views were not those of the trade unions.

Albright might theorize on values and expound his ideals, but at heart he claimed to be a pragmatist. Critical of organized relief to any but the desperately needy, he was even more critical of penal servitude unless the sentence called for hard labor. More to the point, in his understanding, sentences should be served out in the acres of bushland which could well be put to agricultural use and which settlers were invading slowly by dint of ax and grubhoe. Prison camps could aid the country's development, turn a liability into an asset, and the labor would be a stern deterrent to crime. Journalist Albright wrote long

articles on the subject, declared his ideas to governmental
agencies and to schoolhouse audiences.

Apropos, patrons of the old E.D. & B.C. railway will recall
that east of Wanham very tall poplar trees virtually arched over
the railroad track until fires cleared them out and set the stage
for the Wanham Project. Albright, campaigning for his prison
labor proposal one evening while a guest at the E. H. Prevost
home in Wanham, saw his host was not convinced. "Yes," agreed
Mr. Prevost, "prison help could be used to remove the trees
— but Mr. Albright, a box of matches costs fifteen cents!"

It was also in the early 1930's that Albright the poet chose
to portray the busy, industrious, resourceful people of the Peace
with unshaken faith in their country's destiny and in their own
ability to ride out the financial storm. One of his poems reflected
the cheerful, homely ritual of chores:

The march of the seasons brings winter again;
Jack frost binds the streamlets of mountain and glen;
A powder of white over forest and glen
Pronounces a truce in the tillage of men.

The garden is lifted, the potatoes are stored;
The settler has garnered his vegetable hoard.
The threshing is done for which Heaven be thanked;
The stables are mudded, the buildings are banked.

A long winter rest is the city man's dream
Of farmer friends living on honey and cream.
Reality's different, there's wood to be got
And hay to be hauled to the fat-cattle lot.

There's a spring to be opened or water to pump;
Brief daylight keeps choremen quite well on the jump.
The cows must be milked and the hogs must be fed,
The chickens be tended, the horses be bed.

There's grain to be shipped and seed to be cleaned,
And posts to be sharpened and poles to be teamed,
And snowbanks to shovel and coal to be brought,
And logs gotten out on the new building-spot.

And repairs to be done and old harness to mend,
A granary to roof and events to attend.
Before we are ready the winter slips by
And spring once again bids us cropping to try.

The Albright pen served often to buoy up flagging hopes, encourage the discouraged, foster and renew aspirations. In 1941 when the Peace River region was enduring exceptionally adverse harvest weather, he wrote — with apologies to Kipling — thus:

If you can keep a smile when all about you
The pouring rains are rotting all your hay,
While grain is sprouted in the oft-drenched bundles
And cars mire daily on the King's highway;

If you can watch your feed bins running empty
And find no chance to thresh a load of grain;
Can see your fallow greening as a meadow
With weeds and grass, throughout two months of rain;

If you can wade through barnyards miring deeper
And see the pigs convert their lots to mud;
If you can feed a crew and get no work done,
While every hope of fairing proves a dud;

If you can see the sun in broad effulgence
Shine forth as if in promise of fair days,
Then dodge behind a snowy cloud, repentant,
While snow flakes hide his weak and yellow rays;

If you can see a summer's work dissolving,
And face a winter minus feed or cash;
Can still maintain the spirit of Thanksgiving,
When every blessed prospect seems to crash;

If you can stand all this and keep your courage
And cheer a fellow farmer to the end,
Yours is the land and everything that's on it,
And what is more, you are a brick, my friend.

BEAVERLODGE SUB-STATION PERSONNEL

IN HOMESTEAD settlements there is much work to do—and usually finances are very limited for either improvements or living. It is a free life until funds run low; then to the bush or elsewhere for a job.

The Experimental Sub-Station provided work for innumerable settlers in its early years, for a month or for a season. (See Appendix II.) Many prosperous farmers of later days honored time sheets of the "Farm" indicating how each day was spent — pulling weeds, fencing, harvesting plots. One British scion, H. Baring of Barclay's Bank, on a stint in the Colonies doggedly waged war on shepherd's purse one summer in the British tradition of never giving up.

George Baird, father of Bill and Reg, had been well-schooled in the Old Land. As an estate gardener, he respected the Landed Gentry and would conform to their wishes. As the farm foreman at the Beaverlodge Experimental Sub-Station, he implemented Superintendent Albright's wishes, carrying them out with patriotic zeal. His soft, Irish voice may often have masked his true thoughts — until the time he was handed a work order, as long as his arm, by Albright who was to be away for a few days. It would take an army of men in good weather to complete the tasks.

"But Mr. Albright!" exclaimed Baird in a voice of mounting crescendo. "Aren't you ever coming back?"

From tank warfare in the deserts of Egypt, Bill Baird had come to homestead west of Beaverlodge. He was big and strong; roots had to give way to make his fields bigger. But funds ran out so Bill went in search of work. Fortunately the Experimental Farm was nearby and provided him with a grubstake to carry on.

Now, fifty years later his son, Sidney, would be amazed

to fly one of his commercial fleet of helicopters overhead and see the shadow of his father plucking troublesome weeds from the newly seeded Albright lawn.

Bill Baird and Dentist Goodhand made valiant efforts to stock the country with pheasants, with little success. Pheasants must have grit for their gizzards and Peace River snowbanks can be deep.

There were others, such as Jim Bauman with his bluff ways and his kind heart. Somehow his name was associated with the "McLary Brand" — the sear received on backing against a hot stove on bath night. He threshed for Albright once, starting with eighteen plots and ending with seventeen sacks of grain, to the superintendent's perplexity. After supper Jim "found" the missing sack. The crew guessed it was a composite from each of the original lots.

Another employee, Daws Johnson, was shingling a roof one day and spied the new stenographer on her way to work at the Sub-Station office.

"Who's that?" he inquired. He was told.

Finally it came out. "Not much there but the running gear."

A "Twiggy" of yesteryear. Later, that "Twiggy" became his sister-in-law.

When Daws Johnson and his brother Bill went west of Tupper looking for land, a hospitable trapper welcomed them for lunch. "Tie up the horses and come in for a bite. Your wife won't run away."

In the spring of 1927 Dr. Aladar Gedeon came to work at the Station. He had fine clothes, soft hands, and a warm and willing heart. A doctor of science from France and England and at one time a count and youngest member of the Hungarian Parliament, his estate had been confiscated after World War I and he was negotiating with the League of Nations for payment. Meantime, he wrote articles on Canada for European newspapers and sought work.

Dr. Gedeon was a willing worker and very entertaining to a weeding gang in need of stimulation. Came Saturday afternoon and Bill Ross, the blusterous Scottish foreman, told Gedeon to grab a broom and sweep the workroom.

"I shall be pleased to do it," agreed Aladar, "if you will kindly show me how to sweep."

The next week Prof. E. H. Strickland at the University wanted 1,500 wireworms for experimentation. Fine; the Farm had plenty to spare. The ex-count was sent forth to the garden with a jam tin and digging fork. A thunderstorm passed by and Foreman Ross found Aladar under cover.

"Thought I sent you to dig out the wireworms!" he boomed.

"I would gladly do it — but why endanger my health for thirty cents?" was the plaintive reply.

After the Russian invasion of Hungary in 1956 Dr. Gedeon wrote:

> On my return to Hungary I was doing really very well. I bought shares in a factory, became chairman, had a big income and built myself a comfortable home in Budapest in a beautiful part.
>
> After 1945 the factory was nationalized, my shares were taken, lost my position, etc. My house was taken and now, in my 75th year, I am as poor as a church mouse.
>
> I would like to ask you to request a local Ladies' Aid or some other charitable organization to send me a gift parcel. Anything I will gratefully accept, but would especially be happy to have tea, cocoa, coffee, chocolate, soap, washing powder, shaving cream, razor blades, rice, candy, etc.
>
> I am, as far as clothes go, terribly shabby and could use anything but would be very glad to have a pair of warm gloves, crepe-rubber soled shoes (No. 7) a pair of pants (flannel or corduroy — I still remember the good corduroy pants I bought at Gaudin's store) windbreaker (my neck is 41 centimeters) and of course it would top everything to have a sheepskin-lined coat.

His request was referred to the I.O.D.E. (Imperial Order Daughters of the Empire) and a parcel was sent through the International Red Cross. There was no further word from Dr. Gedeon.

One winter, D. M. Kennedy, of Fairview, Federal Member of Parliament and Hereford breeder, hired a young Russian to do chores. At that time, young Vladimir P. Ignatieff — dubbed "Big Jim" at Oxford University — was casting about. After a stint with the Kennedy chores he came to work at the Beaverlodge Experimental Station and from there, to a Ph.D. degree and on to F.A.O. (Food and Agriculture Organization) at Washington and Rome. Today, the name Ignatieff is a byword; brother George is Canada's representative at the United Nations.

Once the outside staff at the Beaverlodge Experimental Sub-Station reached sizeable proportions, individual contact was difficult. So Superintendent Albright went modern and instituted a weekly staff conference.

The office was small but everyone crowded in. The superintendent praised, blamed, criticized, and indulged in philosophical entreaties.

"And now we shall discuss fire protection. Mr. Cussack, what would you do in case of fire?"

The crafty Irishman could fend for himself. The reply was direct. "I'd rush upstairs and get my trunk out." That killed the meeting.

"Upstairs" referred to a bunkroom of moderate size which housed three double beds, an oil stove, and in one corner Assistant Superintendent Stacey's desk, he having fled from the crowded lower office.

At this period, time sheets were required so that the labor charge could be allotted to the proper department, the superintendent could check regularly, and the clerk compile pay lists. Sometimes it took deep thought to state exactly what work had been done; other times the explanation was simply "working." But always the hours were realistic.

Johnny Foster's time sheet was returned for "clarification," a not unusual procedure. It was resubmitted to read: "Ten hours helping Stacey upstairs."

DIRECTOR'S REPORTS

DEPARTMENTAL estimates are a matter of concern to any administrator, but to Superintendent Albright it was a serious trust to receive and to expend public funds. He could not agree that it was no sin to steal from the government or a circus; he demanded extra value for his spending.

The 1926 Estimates reflect his stewardship:

The intention of the Federal Government to launch a vigorous immigration policy looking to the peopling of our vacant areas in general and the Peace River region in particular, amply justifies, in our opinion, a great and immediate expansion of the work at this point. Excellent as the Peace River country is known to be, its settlement and its agriculture nevertheless present many novel and stubborn problems, rendering it doubly necessary for the incoming settler to divest himself of old prejudice and learn his occupation anew under the new conditions. The question is whether the Dominion should allow scores of thousands of settlers to grope their way through these puzzling problems or to assist them with light and leading, such as experimental work provides.

A very wise move was made years ago when sub-stations were established in northern Alberta and the North West Territories. In my humble opinion these sub-stations should be increased in number as suitable incumbents can be found.

There should, in my opinion, be such sub-stations, distinct from illustration stations, established forthwith within the Fort St. John District, one in Pouce Coupe, one or two in the Athabasca River region, one in the Liard valley and the work at the Great Slave points and at Fort Smith should, if possible, be amplified. Practically all these points are or shortly will be, objectives of immigration.

As time passes and the vastness of the opportunity for service impresses me with additional force year by year, I have come to the conclusion that nothing should be permitted to stand in the way of considerable extension, especially along horticultural lines.

FIELD HUSBANDRY

Wages	$ 250.00
Gasoline and Oils	15.00
Equipment:	
Wind gauge, hygro-thermograph, thermometers, say	300.00
Total	$ 565.00

SOIL FERTILITY INVESTIGATIONS

Wages	$ 600.00
Sacks, receptacles, etc.	50.00
Total	$ 650.00

CEREALS

Wages		$1,000.00
Machinery & Equipment:		
100 Stook covers (60 x 72 ins.)	175.00	
4 Tarpaulins with rings	75.00	
Rod Row thresher	30.00	
Clipper Cleaner	30.00	
Pneumatic device for cleaning separator, say	110.00	420.00
Gasoline and oils		50.00
Seeds that may have to be purchased		20.00
Total		$1,490.00

FORAGE CROPS

Wages		$ 800.00
Gasoline and oils		20.00
Machinery and Equipment:		
Material for drying racks	100.00	
Device for edging plots (if invented) say	100.00	
Machinery for threshing, hulling and scarifying small seeds, say	400.00	600.00
Total		$1,420.00

HORTICULTURE

Wages	$1,500.00
Tools and supplies	100.00
Distribution of stock	50.00
Total	$1,650.00

APIARY

Wages .... $ 60.00
Equipment:
    4 Hive bodies and foundations 25.00

                           Total .... $ 85.00

EXTENSION AND PUBLICITY

Equipment and photography, lantern slides, etc. $ 350.00
Exhibitions and excursion or picnics 100.00
Travelling expenses 150.00

                           Total .... $ 600.00

GENERAL

Expenditure, estimated $6,000.00

Justification

With the enlargement of work in various lines, a greatly increased demand upon clerical service is created and it has been found necessary to press some of the better-educated laborers in to chart and tabulate records, calculations, etc., and with the growth of the work and its development along the lines of marginal elimination and dry matter determinations, all of which involves much increase in figuring, either an additional clerk or a mechanical calculator is badly needed. We are doing more and better investigational work every year but there is a safety limit to human energy.

For the supervision of outside work a foreman is badly needed, though no special allowance for this is included in our estimates.

While appropriations were being expended, authorities at headquarters in Ottawa were required to know how the crop was developing and other information which might be interesting to the Minister of Agriculture and his advisors. Consequently each week a prescribed form was filled at the Beaverlodge Station and dispatched.

A compilation of miscellaneous notes contributes to the Albright portrait and his service to agriculture:

October 13, 1923

The past season here has been a magnificent example of the fact that it pays a farmer, instead of consuming himself with worry about markets and weather, to go ahead and 'saw wood'. Until near the middle of June conditions could scarcely have been more disheartening. Cutworms and grasshoppers fought for what little growth there was. In dogged desperation we fought these with poison and saved the threatened crops for the most part. Then came the July rains just in time.

For the amount of moisture available, growth has been truly wonderful. I do not think the prairie has ever before had such lashions of feed.

Experimental work has always taken precedence here and we let our stand of commercial crop stand until last week. Sometimes the experimental work almost gets my goat, but so long as we do it at all we intend to do it right.

January 5, 1924
At the urgent solicitation of Deputy Craig and Mr. W. J. Stephen I judged grain at the Lake Saskatoon Seed Fair. The exhibit was large and of most excellent quality. As my expenses were only a dollar, I did not put in a bill to the Provincial Department but told them to regard it as an act of Interdepartmental co-operation.

February 6, 1926
The most unsatisfactory crop this year is the ice harvest. Snow in early winter kept the ice thin and chinooks later broke it up in the streams. Kindly communicate this to Mr. Rothwell who laughed at me for suggesting that chinooks interfered with hockey.

April 3
We had a successful series of meetings under the auspices of the Pouce Coupe Creamery Association, speaking at six points, with a total attendance of 290. The meetings covered chiefly horticulture and forage crops and were illustrated with lantern slides illuminated by our new 6-volt lamps, the battery being at times recharged by special equipment on the car. They lasted from two-and-a-quarter to three-and-a-half hours. At the final meeting in the soldier settlement across the Cutbank I am sure they would have listened for another hour or two but I considered enough as good as a feast. Many questions were asked and I received 23 requests for a start in small fruits and ornamentals and 12 for co-operative experiments in inoculation of alfalfa.

April 10
On Friday evening April 9 we responded to a two-year-old invitation from the Buffalo Lakes neighbourhood, about 25 miles northeast of here, by giving a lantern-slide lecture on our work. By using the car we were able to take in

this event without using more than a couple of hours of working time.

July 24
Had nearly 30 carloads of visitors during the week. Practically all came from distances of from 60 to 75 miles. A number were from Berwyn and other points north of the Peace. Scarcely any were city people philandering about the grounds, but at least 90 per cent were farmers who were keenly interested in the work.

August 14
In spite of an early date it seemed advisable this year to prepare an exhibit for the circuit of five fairs: Grande Prairie, Lake Saskatoon, Spirit River, Waterhole and Berwyn. It showed some very fine growth, including a stalk of sweet clover about 8 feet tall, a sheaf of alfalfa about 4 feet tall, as well as grains.

August 21
The bees continue to do excellent work and the colony on scales is now up to 491 pounds. Its net 24-hour intake on Sunday was 20.5 pounds.

October 9
A few plot yields follow:

Legacy oats	139 bus. per acre
Liberty (hulless)	94 bus. per acre
Marquis wheat	63 bus. per acre
Red Bobs	71 bus. per acre

February 5, 1927
Demand for articles on the Peace River country is insatiable. Just after finishing one for Olds Agricultural School, came a like request from the Vermilion school. The *Family Herald* and *Grain Growers' Guide* want articles and during the week I wrote three press articles. Meantime, data for the annual reports are being tabulated.

October 15
From Spirit River yields of 55, 52 and 49 bushels of wheat are reported from three different farms, with 28 outfits working in that limited district. From Dawson Creek comes the report that J. C. Hall threshed 3200 bushels of wheat off 75 acres. He also had 11 acres of Garnet going 63.2 bushels per acre.

At Lower Beaverlodge H. W. Allen, MLA, had 10 acres of Ruby in 1926 which went 55 bus. per acre. He fall-plowed the stubble and drilled in Ruby this spring again, without other cultivation. It yielded 40 bushels per acre in 1927.

In the same neighbourhood A. Sherk and Sons had 30 acres of Ruby which went 50 bus. per acre despite very heavy waste by lodging. Thirty acres of summerfallow went 52 bushels. The biggest wheat yield thus far reported from the western part of Grande Prairie is by Earl Cage, northwest of Halcourt. A measured acre yielded 78.2 bushels per acre.

December 10
The peas with which Herman Trelle won reserve championship at Chicago were Chancellor which we gave him last spring, representing several years of our own propagation.

December 17
Saturday's mail brought 9 inquiries about the Peace River Country from four provinces and one state. I cannot conscientiously advise people to homestead until more land is brought within reach of steel.

February 13, 1928
An article quoted from the Financial Post, says American capitalists plan to link Chicago and Alaska via the Peace. Considerable circumstantial evidence goes to confirm this.

April 7
On April 5 Mr. Stacey and the Superintendent gave a lantern-slide lecture at Percy school house. Roads horrible. Got home at 4 a.m.

July 28
After a steady stream of visitors and local picnics, we entertained on Saturday 28th a body of about 425 people including the Edmonton Board of Trade. That evening Dr. McRostie and I left for Fort St. John. Rain caught us there on the return. The ferry was found downstream transporting the stranded Edmonton Board of Trade to the D.A. Thomas, grounded 24 miles down stream. We had to wait until Tuesday morning to get across but by driving in relays, managed to get Dr. McRostie to the train at Sexsmith with an hour to spare. Some of the Edmonton Board of Trade spent two nights without shelter and with very scant fare.

August 25
On Saturday we were visited by the C.P.R. Party, headed by President E. W. Beatty, accompanied by Sir Herbert Holt, Director C.P.R. and president of the Royal Bank of Canada; Sir Charles Gordon, president of the Bank of Montreal; Beaudry Lehman, general manager, Banque Canadienne Nationale; D. C. Coleman, vice-president C.P.R. in charge of western lines; Hon. Senator Smeaton

White of Montreal, president of the Montreal Gazette Publishing Co.; W. A. Black, director C.P.R. and president, Ogilvie Flour Mills Co. Ltd.; Sir Henry Cockshutt, ex-Lieutenant Governor of Ontario, director C.P.R. and president Cockshutt Plow Co; F. W. Molson, director C.P.R. and part-owner of Molson's Brewery; W. H. Tilley, K.C., director C.P.R.; R. H. McMaster, director, C.P.R., president and director of the Steel Company of Canada; J. A. Richardson, director, C.P.R., president and general manager of Jas. A. Richardson & Sons Ltd; and Dr. W. W. Chipman of Montreal.

It would appear that practically all the prominent business men, administrators and men of affairs in Canada have now been here this year or are about to be, save only the Director of Experimental Farms and it is respectfully suggested that he should climax the list by visiting the district before the snow flies.

October 27
On Saturday the 27th, Mr. Stacey and the Superintendent attended an organization meeting in Grande Prairie where 42 shares of $25.00 each were subscribed toward the stock of a Grande Prairie Seed Growers' Association to handle, especially, registered seed and commercial seed closely descended therefrom. It was a help and encouragement to know that the Station was to be provided this year with a seed cleaning plant.

December 1
Alex and William Thomson have each sold a carload of Garnet wheat in Wembley, getting a grade of No. 2. Their yield was around 45 bushels per acre. Another neighbor on higher land intended to sow Garnet last spring but changed his mind and sowed Marquis instead. He is a pretty good farmer too, but his wheat graded only No. 6 because of frosted kernels. The concensus of opinion in their neighborhood is that the Beaverlodge Station is right in recommending the sowing of good early kinds.

March 2
The Station is co-operating in putting on with Mr. A. R. Judson, district representative of the Provincial Department, a series of local meetings urging farmers to sow as much as possible of their new breaking to registered and high-class commercial seed grain.

March 23
During the week the Superintendent responded to two standing invitations from Blueberry Mountain, a soldier settlement 25 miles northwest of Spirit River and Fairview

(superseding Waterhole) 36 miles northeast of Spirit River, holding two good meetings at each point, the Fairview meetings being in co-operation with Mr. Judson. To do this and to interview the Railway Commission representative he covered in three days 176 miles by E.D. & B.C., 122 by trail, spoke from the platform about eight hours and in conversation as much more and averaged about 5 hours sleep each night for the first four nights of the week and returned to find an accumulation of 79 letters.

April 13
By invitation the Superintendent spent the whole week in Pouce Coupe District addressing three afternoon and six evening meetings. As roads were breaking up the trip proved rather expensive but was highly successful. The attendance was excellent, three of the six points turning out about 90 per cent of the local residents. The evening meetings were interspersed with a few patriotic sing-songs, the words being illuminated on the screen. One farmer who drove 10 miles through mud said he would have come twice as far rather than miss the four-hour program and many, after sitting for hours on hard benches declared that they were ready to listen to more.

April 20
Addressed two meetings at Debolt, 15 miles east of the Smoky River and one at Teepee Creek, west of the Smoky. This makes about the 23rd meeting this year for the Superintendent, besides half-a-dozen covered by Mr. Stacey. To reach Debolt it was necessary to cross the ice on foot and hire a team. Rested four hours on a schoolhouse floor and hurried back to re-cross the river before the rotting ice should break up.

August 17
Had visits from J. C. Moynan, Dr. Ray Neidig and J. W. Marritt and took them to Fort St. John and afterward inspected all the co-operative phosphate tests in this area. Had a very good field day at Abbott's Illustration Station, Fort St. John, with 65 much interested visitors, practically all farmers and their families.

Dr. Neidig found no positive results from phosphate on the light-coloured soil where it was tried on the station but increased yields on wheat fields of Sherk and Trelle and appreciable benefit on one oat field across the Red Willow River. Further tests seem warranted.

A week ago we had the advanced Geography Class under Prof. Colby of the University of Chicago.

Correspondence included an appreciative letter of Vilhjalmur Stefansson regarding life in the Arctic.

September 14

Col. J. S. Dennis, president, Canada Colonization Association, with a party of C.P.R. officials, visited the Station. They were apparently well pleased with the experimental work but were told here as at Grande Prairie that the Peace River region did not welcome efforts to pump in immigration. What it wanted was physical facilities such as railroads, etc., and immigration would take care of itself. Settlers are already too far ahead of steel.

September 21

G. H. Hiffernan of Rolla, B.C. reports that 25 acres of Reward averaged 46 bushels, his best 10 acres yielding 60 bushels per acre and grading No. 1 at Hythe elevators.

November 16

The Peace River District enters the winter with the most propitious outlook on record. The subsoil is stored with moisture to an extraordinary degree. A fairly good crop has been threshed in good condition, for the most part, the grain grading mostly 2 and 3 Northern with a little No. 1 Northern and an odd car of No. 1 Hard.

November 23

Wire from Toronto indicates following winnings by Peace River exhibitors at the 1929 Royal Winter Fair:

> Spring wheat, W. D. Albright, second on sample Reward
> Oats, Robert Cochrane, Grande Prairie, fourth,
>   presumably Victory
> Peas, Robert Cochrane, fifth.

With reference to wheat, Mr. Albright's sample was prepared from a bulk lot in the granary, threshed by a custom outfit the day preceding the commencement of the September storm. The preparation was mostly done by his daughter Eileen Albright, assisted by a little hired help and coached as necessary by Mr. E. C. Stacey.

January 18, 1930

The Superintendent returned from Ottawa on Friday evening's train, having addressed in Edmonton a small meeting of the Canadian League at the University there on subject of Peace River colonization. He also gave interviews on the same subject in Toronto and London.

January 25

Enclosed herewith is a clipping "High Prairie Honors G. W. Randall for showing he made at Chicago show."

February 1
Who says people don't read our reports? R. B. Brown
of Grimshaw writes: 'I am a newcomer to this district and
would be glad to receive your latest report of your Station.
I had a chance to look over one in Saskatchewan last summer
and it was very interesting and sold me on this North Country.'

February 15
Under date of January 1, Charles G. Jones, our co-operator
at Gold Bar, B.C., writes: 'Mr. Swanell of the P.G.E. Survey,
camped here nearly a month and asked me for a report
on grain, gardening, etc. I gave it to him, also samples
of grain. He took several snaps of the garden and was
highly pleased with the growth here, especially of the berries, to which I gave them carte blanche and of which they
gathered 5 to 10 lbs. each day for their table, beside what
they ate from the canes and at that we couldn't pick half
of them.'
(Note: Mr. Jones' farm was in that part of the valley of
the Peace which has been flooded to fill Lake Williston.)

April 19
Enclosed herewith you will find a copy of the issue of
the Grande Prairie Herald, April 18. Please note article
marked 'Sixty Carloads of New Settlers Came North Last
Week.'

May 31
The Superintendent could not resist an unholy wish that
Dr. Grisdale might have accompanied him on the 100-mile
trip from Grimshaw north to Clear Hills and return, bump-
ing over sunken corduroy, tearing through mud holes, etc.
In one case the chained wheels kicked back the poles of
a bridge until by the time the car was across it, a gap a
yard wide was following immediately behind the car.
This 100 miles took more out of the car than 1,000 of
ordinary travelling.

June 7
The enclosed item from the Grande Prairie Herald reports
797 homestead entries and 52 soldier grants at the Peace
River and Grande Prairie Land Agencies during May.

July 26
The Superintendent returned Saturday evening by rail from
Waterways, having had a very busy but very profitable,
very enjoyable and rejuvenating trip to Herschel Island.
A surprising amount of gardening was discovered clear to
Aklavik.

A large number of men were found who were interested in co-operative experiments and great appreciation was manifest on every hand that the Department of Agriculture was taking an active interest in the region. An immense amount of data of an impressive character was gathered which will take two or three weeks' work to get into shape. The trip was without serious mishap of any kind and Flying Officer Uhlman did his best to comprehend the missions of all. He even planned a side trip to Liard, but threatening weather on the appointed day prevented this. As it was, the most promising regions available for further settlement were not touched at all, but very encouraging data was obtained from what might be considered the less promising regions.

During the week, accompanied by Ignatieff and Godfrey of the staff the Superintendent visited the Illustration Station at Baldonnel, Fort St. John District, where a very successful field day was held. The Superintendent demonstrated the construction of a root harrow and the use of stumping powder for blasting rock and willows. Mr. Abbott gave the results of a very satisfactory test of tractor versus horse breaking, confessing himself a complete convert to the tractor method of breaking scrub land.

August 9
On Thursday, 7th, the party visited Rose Prairie at the northern edge of the Montney prairie, where about 50 people assembled to a banquet luncheon, after which they proceeded to North Pine where the previous day's demonstrations were repeated before about 50 settlers, followed in the evening by a lantern-slide lecture for which 185 assembled, though not all could enter the Hall, 20 × 30 feet.

All told, the trip was exceedingly successful even though we did wreck a car battery on a grass-hidden rock on a prairie trail and dodged stumps every rod or two of the last mile. Reached Abbott's at 8:00 a.m. Friday, rested two or three hours, then obtained photos and notes and reached home at 10:30 p.m.

"TIMELY HINTS"

IT WAS always a pleasure to open the morning mail and read letters from farmers requesting advice. But by the end of each week, the correspondence file was bulking up and other work was pressing.

The answer was that as problems of one farmer were problems of others, many of whom had neither time to write nor the ability to put well-formulated thoughts on paper, the letters should be handled collectively, rather than individually.

Thus "Timely Hints" was born in 1928. The column was syndicated to some twenty newspapers from Edmonton north and to the District Agriculturists of the Peace. It was not surprising that each issue carried the caption "It is a pleasure as well as a duty to serve."

Writing the column was comparatively easy for the first few issues, but there were times when the files had to be searched carefully and diligently. Also there were holidays and business trips to intervene. What did it matter if there was a break now and then in issue?

Often journalist Albright found himself competing with his other selves — economist, poet, philosopher, citizen-at-large. "Timely Hints" mirrored his entire thinking. If the weather was cold he counseled to warm the horses' bits or look to the woodpile. Throughout the depression years he preached better times ahead and for the present "be frugal."

Gleanings from "Timely Hints" do much to portray the Albright character and personality:

July 2, 1932
One of the most valuable sciences any of us can learn is the science of doing without.

July 21
In the estimation of a man the first question should be "does he ring true?"

September 29
As this is written oats are quoted locally at 9c a bushel. Query: "Can grain be worth less than nothing?"

November 3
Animal comfort is the greatest condition powder ever.

November 10
Three Creeks built a neat 22 x 26 log schoolhouse with a cash outlay not exceeding $130 for the school itself and opened it with a sumptuous chicken supper. Where there's a will there's a way.

November 16
"My hens have ceased laying," explained a homesteader, "because they can't lay hollow eggs. This year I have only hollow wheat to feed them."

November 17
When what one has to sell possesses no value to speak of, the necessary alternative is to buy less.

November 24
> *Snow beautifies the landscape*
> *And purifies the air;*
> *Protects perennial plant life*
> *In cold zones everywhere.*

December 1
"Depression" has been wittily defined as "doing without things our fathers never knew."

December 22
The value of smiles has not deflated. They have seldom been worth more than they are now.

January 5, 1933
Unless the world learns the danger of uncurbed inflation and reckless borrowing it will recover from the present depression only to ride for a harder fall.

January 12
Are the horses' bits wrapped with canvas?
Envy is the canker of happiness. When all are rich, none is rich. When all are poor, none is poor. What good times we are having!

January 19
The triumph of life lies not in the felicity of circumstances but rather in the way trying circumstances are met.

January 26
Integrity is priceless.

There is more downright satisfaction in paying a debt than in collecting one.

Another rabbit trap has been invented by a well-known wag of the Halcourt-Beaverlodge district. He puts out a candle and the rabbits stare at it so hard that their eyes water and the tears running down freeze them to the ground. Next?

A correspondent from Sunset House complains that the rabbits won't co-operate. They don't cry. The farmers do when they look at their feed stacks.

February 2
Depression teaches us that many necessities are unnecessary.

February 9
In the battle of life one is hardly beaten until he gives up.

Knud Lang, who ripened oats and barley in the Mackenzie Delta in 1932, explains that his flats were about 12 miles south and three miles west of Aklavik, being 1317 miles north of the 49th parallel.

February 18
Mr. A. B. Belanger of Dreau recalls that 15 years ago people who were supposed to be learned, were telling him that no one could make a living on the lands he had been farming for the past four years.

January weather readings at a few representative points show the January mean temperature to have been quite "mean" enough.

March 2
Fretting does no good and much harm.

The last push puts the barrow over the hump. Never give up.

March 9
I do not need that I can't afford.

By the laws of compensation we should be due for a fine summer.

March 23
As between snowbanks and earthquakes, our choice is clear; the banks are softer.

> *Grey skies and skirling clouds of white;*
> *Filled trails and sleigh-tracks of great height;*
> *Piled drifts, unbroken fields of snow;*
> *Cold months and winter dragging slow.*
> *'Twill not be always thus. The sun will shine,*
> *The fields be bare; snow-melt seek Arctic brine.*
> *The seeds will sprout, the birds again will sing.*
> *Be cheerful, all, and ready for the spring!*

April 20
Earthquakes in the early hours! The rapidly growing seedlings lift the surface and a plant breaks through. The everlasting miracle of spring.

April 27
It has been a great winter for keeping meat.

September 14
"In the early days we could hardly ripen oats in the Red Deer district," said Alfred Speakman, MP. "Today wheat is a stable crop. I do not know that land clearing and cultivation change the general climate but crop production becomes safer."

September 24
Credit is the foster mother of debt. Credit is a dove. Debt is a raven.

October 26
From the appearance of many straw piles it should be unnecessary to put green goggles on the cattle this winter.

A Nampa woman attended an evening meeting from a point four miles distant. Five years they had lived without a road to town. Now a road has been chopped but not graded.

A damp berth is poison to a pig.

January 4, 1934
Has the world really learned the lesson of the depression? If not, it will surely repeat.

Perhaps the crime of lending money has been somewhat overstressed. The folly of borrowing heavily is more to the point.

February 22
A job put off is a drag until it is finished. One can get into weed trouble fast enough without sowing it.

March 4
March came as a lamb. Will it --------?
Keep livestock. Keep good livestock. But not too much.

April 12
"Do you answer questions?" began a recent inquirer's apologetic address. After 30 years of professional life, during which some 20,000 to 40,000 questions have been answered by letter and in print, this interrogation prompted an excusable smile.

May 3
Once seeding is over, rake the door-yard and straighten the woodpile.

May 17
The Lower Plains are witnessing the truth of the warning "Sow the wind and reap the whirlwind."

June 14
If order is Heaven's first law, there are some farmers that are none too heavenly.

June rains, June sunshine, June verdure, June roses; it is good these days to be alive.

So far as feasible we plan to avoid striking the same rock twice. Carry a bar on the plough.

August 23
Verily the loads of currants and saskatoons this year have to be seen to be believed.

Horsetail is a wet-land weed; foxtail an habiture of dry, alkaline soil. Both tails are tales of woe.

Showers fill the wheat kernels until they are in danger of bursting. Popcorn we have; pop wheat we are in danger of having.

A hundredweight of honey per acre or more can be harvested by a single colony of bees from alsike, white Dutch or sweet clover blossoms.

September 6
"It takes nature not less than 400 years to build one inch of top soil" states H. H. Bennett of the United States Bureau of Chemistry and Soils.

September 20
Perhaps if the patient were left alone, old ailing business might recover more quickly.

September snow storms are like barking dogs. The bite is seldom as bad as the threat appears.

On the Pouce Coupe Illustration Station one stalk of

rhubarb weighed 1 pound 13 ounces and made two quarts of preserves.

October 4
If winter comes we may be able to thresh. Under trying conditions good work tells — stooking, for instance.

October 11
For all the carloads of relief produce shipped eastward, the enlarging of root cellars has been a favourite sport — between showers.

When the worst comes to the worst, it takes about six men, standing in a row telling hard-luck stories, to keep each other cheered up.

Misery loves company but sometimes the misery gets so deep that you hope the other fellow is escaping.

November 1
Weather? What's the use!

November 8
It appears that after having done our work all through the summer between showers, we shall have to do our threshing between snowstorms.

November 15
From a punster's standpoint, is not Winnipeg a logical place at which to peg wheat prices?

January 5, 1935
Beekeeping is the only honest way of stealing a living. The neighbor's fields supply the harvest.

February 14
> *Across the black of the Arctic night*
> *Glimmer the rays of the Northern Light*
> *Discerned at first as a fainting sheen*
> *Darting and dancing their colours gleam.*

It takes quite a man to weigh 200 pounds — but not much of a pig.

March 21
The Russians have a saying: 'Haste is only good for catching flies.' Haste can be overdone, but hustle is needed at all times.

June 6
Diversity is a bulwark against disaster.

Strange that a man who can operate a tractor or combine successfully often exhibits inability in adjusting and using the one-horse cultivator.

June 13
"It is fortunate," reflects an acquaintance, "that no man has the making of the weather or there would be an awful war about it." The umpire would be killed.

June 27
> *When it snows, snows, snows, snows, snows,*
> *Seems as if the ground would never get bare again;*
> *When it rains, rains, rains, rains, rains,*
> *Seems as if 'twould never dry up again.*
>
> *When it blows, blows, blows, blows, blows,*
> *Seems as if 'twould never get calm again.*
> *When it's dry, dry, dry, dry, dry,*
> *Seems as if it never would rain again.*
> *But it does, it does, it does.*
> *Why worry?*

July 18
Great truths are usually simple to state and easy to comprehend.
Whether at home or away from home, a man is better for a bath, a shave and a Sunday's change of clothes. He feels more like a man.

July 25
What incense sweeter than the smell of new mown hay?

August 1
Immersionists should be at home in the Lesser Slave Lake region.
"Cedar swamps of corn" was a picturesque expression of the late Senator Dan Derbyshire. Swamps of brome and sweet clover we have.

August 29
George Bouffioux of Fort St. John comments on ploughing alfalfa. "You can't kill the stuff," agreeing also that it is a nice kind of weed.

September 5
Beneath his white robe Jack Frost carries a black hand.

October 4
> *Crisp morning, golden, winey afternoon,*
> *Gilt evening, summer passing much too soon.*

October 24
Calf fat is more easily kept than restored.
Anyone can quit. It takes strength of purpose to carry on.

November 28
Graciously referring to "Timely Hints" as a tonic, a Sexsmith correspondent dubiously alludes to a recent item suggesting that things could be worse. With tough oats at 6c a bushel and 5c for threshing them, he fails to see how.

Another observes his chickens "walk over the threshed wheat looking for feed."

January 2, 1936
Some day somebody is going to try to figure out the cost of credit.

January 31
The silent spruce in sparkling snow arrays
Her bending boughs throughout the passing days.
The forest robed in rime of fretted frost,
With silver brilliance glistens, gem-embossed.

February 6
British kings are farmers. Farmers, kings.

February 20
The lazy windmill turns its tilted vanes
In vocal protest as the winter wanes;
In cold, in storm, it fills the brimming tanks;
The busy choreman proffers it his thanks.

March 12
As out toward the Rocky peaks we look
Mirage portends approach of soft chinook.
Irony of fate is the near failure of the ice harvest! Too cold to cut it in February; too much water on it in March. Might as well live in the tropics.

March 26
Sod is the sponge that soaks up running water.

April 6
Our friend, the $16.00 hog!

June 18
Two things the enumerators have forgotten to count are the mosquitoes and the flies.

June 25
Some years ago, in drafting an annual report, the sub-station apiarist "regretted" that dandelions had been too few.
When the ground grows grey and arid 'twixt the rows
of wilting grain,
How good it feels to listen to the dashing of the rain,
The booming of the thunder and the flashing of the bolt,
The booming, flashing, splashing gives the farmer renewed
hope.

July 16
Some of us are so busy doing things that we don't get much done.

October 1
At least the bad weather afforded a chance to dig the potatoes.

October 8
Breezes flirting with the east are not reassuring at threshing time.

October 15
Silvery tissues of cobweb over the fallow land spun,
Carry the eye on a filmy path into the morning sun.

November 5
No one knows so much but that someone else knows more.

November 12
Where snow lies Jack Frost treads lightly.
Despoilers do not love the country they have ravished.

November 26
Good soil is a product of the ages. It will stand abuse but not forever.

June 10, 1937
Trouble with advice is that those who need it don't take it.

June 24
When wheat prices mount, most of us lose our heads. When depression ensues, we begin looking for them.

September 17
The beauty of the autumn and the splendor of
*   the dawn,*
The gold upon the hillsides and the dew upon
*   the lawn;*
The mellow tints of ripeness and the azure of
*   the days,*
The winey, heady incense is a memory that stays.

October 8
Breath of gold on the hillside,
Regal tints on the plain.

October 21
When the yellows change to orange
Etched with brown and splashed with crimson,
Then the rich ripe tints of autumn
Mark the turning of the year.

Within the memory of men now living, land in the Ohio Valley region has been cleared, tilled, ruined by erosion and abandoned.

November 19
> *Wraith of fog in the valley,*
> *Flurry of snow on the plain,*
> *Freckle of white in the forest*
> *Fresco of frost on the pane.*

December 2
Recipe for neighborhood harmony: Expect the best from each other, not the worst.

December 16
If Peace River exhibitors fail to take championships at the Toronto Royal — that's news.

January 6, 1938
How much do I owe? How much do I own? The balance sheet will tell.

January 20
> *What wheat to sow?*
> *What crops to grow?*
> *To fertilize,*
> *To hybridize,*
> *Or realize*
> *It's mostly wise*
> *To stabilize?*

June 9
It is always too soon to despair.

June 16
In a dry time every day brings rain 24 hours nearer.

August 18
"A good year in which to have a poor crop" is one farmer's philosophical allusion to the price situation.

October 20
Walt Mason's Rippling Rhymes remind us "there is no sense in starting up a row about your car, your crowbar or your cow." Well said.

October 27
No human artist ever painted such a sunrise as greeted the eye at Beaverlodge on the morning of October 20.

Threshing at Stoney Point, the Rutabaga Johnson farm, Beaverlodge, 1911. The power sweep belonged to O. H. Johnson and the separator, the first in the Beaverlodge Valley, was owned by the Beaverlodge Industrial Co. Ltd.

The threshing outfit of the Beaverlodge Industrial Co. Ltd. moving to a new site. This outfit was purchased in 1914 and freighted in over the Edson Trail.

A tour of the plots by the United Farmers of Alberta picnic group, Beaverlodge Experimental Sub-Station. 1921.

The Charles McNaught and Dan Chambers families on the Edson Trail, 1912.

A mud hole on the Grouard Trail, 1913. Some settlers would tell that the mud hole was 100 miles long! — W. D. Albright photo

The metamorphosis of a hog house, the W. D. Albright residence, 1918, 1922, and 1940. Experimental Station, Beaverlodge. — W. D. Albright photos

LANTERN-SLIDE
LECTURE
"Not by Bread Alone"
BY W. D. ALBRIGHT

**Superintendent, Dominion Experimental Sub-station
BEAVERLODGE, ALBERTA**

On _AUGUST 13, 1931._
(Date)

At _NORTH PINE SCHOOL_
(Name of Hall)

NORTH PINE, B.C. At _8 P.M._ o'clock sharp
(Name of Town)   (Hour)

Mr. Albright will give a lecture on the above subject illustrated with an excellent series of slides made chiefly from photographs taken on the Beaverlodge Station, along with some other well chosen views.

The address is essentially a plea for horticulture, home-making, full living, and worthy citizenship, accompanied by some cultural directions based upon local experience.

The lecture will be held under the auspices of _NORTH PINE FARMERS INSTITUTE_

(Signed) _Jas. Young_

W. D. Albright lectured extensively to farm groups. — C. R. Elliott photo

More than 200 persons gathered for supper, the Albright lecture, and dance at the North Pine School in B.C. August 13, 1931, under the auspices of the North Pine Women's Institute. — W. D. Albright photo

The Illustration Station annual field day on the farm of William Perkins, Debolt, was always lively. The group of 1942. — W. D. Albright photo

Part of the group attending the Illustration Station field day, August 14, 1933, on the farm of Alex McKenzie, Fairview, across the highway from the present Agricultural and Vocational School. — W. D. Albright photo

A group of students from Toronto and Montreal retraced the footsteps of the early explorers down the Parsnip and Peace rivers under the guidance of Nicholas Ignatieff. Here seen visiting the farm of Herman Trelle, Wembley, 1937. — W. D. Albright photo

This group from Blueberry Mountain came 100 miles in an open truck to visit the Beaverlodge Experimental Station, August 11, 1941. — W. D. Albright photo

The Sudeten settlers at Tomslake, B.C. on a field day at the Beaverlodge Experimental Station, 1946. — W. D. Albright photo

Dr. and Mrs. G. Turesson, of Sweden, and Dr. L. E. Kirk, Ottawa, on the Athabasca ferry, 1934. — W. D. Albright photo

United States Vice-President Henry A. Wallace, Superintendent W. D. Albright, and Major David R. Nelson at the Grande Prairie Airport, July 7, 1944.

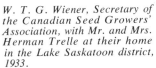

W. T. G. Wiener, Secretary of the Canadian Seed Growers' Association, with Mr. and Mrs. Herman Trelle at their home in the Lake Saskatoon district, 1933.

Ceremonial party at the unveiling of the Albright Cairn, Beaverlodge Experimental Station. L-R: Corp. Frank Smith, R.C.M.P., Dr. Morden Long, Victor Flint, Robert Cochrane, Gordon Albright, William Grant, Alex Ross, Harvey Tuffill, E. C. Stacey, Const. Amos Bramhill, R.C.M.P. September 15, 1954. — A. A. Guitard photo

WILLIAM DONALD ALBRIGHT
"THE FUTURE OF CANADA LIES IN
ITS BREADTH"
BORN AT SOUTH CAYUGA, ONT.
15TH AUGUST, 1881
EDITOR, "THE FARMERS' ADVOCATE" 1908-13
ORGANIZER AND FIRST SUPERINTENDENT
OF THIS EXPERIMENTAL STATION
FOR THIRTY-ONE YEARS HE HELPED
NOTABLY TO SHAPE THE AGRICULTURAL
PATTERN OF THE PEACE RIVER COUNTRY
DIED AT HANEY, B.C., 1ST MAY, 1946

ERECTED BY THE GOVERNMENT OF CANADA
HISTORIC SITES AND MONUMENTS BOARD

The plaque, Albright Cairn. — A. A. Guitard photo

December 8
Perhaps we shall have such another winter as that of 1925-26
when there were only 12 sub-zero nights at Beaverlodge,
with the lowest register -11 degrees on October 26.

Mark Twain wrote of life along the Mississippi, Will Rogers
talked about the common man, and Gregory Clark reported
social trends in terms of the fisherman. W. D. Albright, too,
was a Humanist. His locale was the Peace but his concern was
the People. Thus his philosophies have a universal appeal, far
beyond the daily concerns of his immediate surroundings.

IN MEMORIAM

WHILE still in his prime, W. D. Albright became afflicted with Parkinson's Disease about the start of World War II. He carried on as well as he could with patriotic zeal until forced to retire and with Mrs. Albright, to seek the more equitable climate of Haney, B.C. He was buried at Beaverlodge in 1946.

The Historic Sites and Monuments Board of Canada, with Dr. Morden H. Long as Alberta representative, saw fit to honor Albright with a cairn on his beloved Station, bearing the inscription:

WILLIAM DONALD ALBRIGHT
"THE FUTURE OF CANADA LIES IN
ITS BREADTH"
Born at South Cayuga, Ont.
15th August, 1881
Editor "The Farmers' Advocate" 1903-13
Organizer and First Superintendent
Of This Experimental Station.
For Thirty-One Years He Helped
Notably To Shape the Agricultural
Pattern of the Peace River Country
Died at Haney, B.C. 1st May, 1946

Tribute to Mr. Albright's work was recorded by E. C. Stacey, his co-worker for more than twenty years:

It is Mr. Albright's record that he worked for the most economical agricultural development of the district. He showed what could be done and demonstrated how to do it. His constant message was that this was a land of opportunity and that development carried with it very definite obligations. He sought to have comfortable homes built with well-planted grounds. He preached the permanency of agriculture. By press and contact he told Canada that the Peace River region was a very great asset.

We are inclined to take things for granted. We now accept our early-maturing varieties of cereals. We accept alfalfa and sweet clover with satisfactory methods of inoculation. We accept soil conservation practices. We accept apples, crabapples, plums and small fruits and may realize that pears and apricots are now being grown to some extent 413 miles north of the International Border. We accept the saskatoon as a hedge plant and may know that the Station has developed a choice selection of this native fruit. We accept information on more than 100 adapted ornamental trees and shrubs.

Mr. Albright devoted most of a lifetime to these and kindred subjects. He has had assistance but full credit is given him for pioneering the work of the Station and in maintaining active leadership until forced to relinquish his work.

The press of September 23, 1954, carried the story of unveiling the Albright tablet and cairn on the Beaverlodge Experimental Station grounds, under the heading "National Historical Site Marked for W. D. Albright."

A dismal, grey day made greyer by fine, cold rain and a raw, fall wind chilled none of the heartfelt warmth with which pioneers of the Peace River country, congregating at the Dominion Experimental Station Wednesday afternoon, September 15, paid tribute to an old friend and neighbor and one of the truly great men of western Canada, William Donald Albright, first Superintendent.

The occasion marked the unveiling of the tablet and cairn erected by the Historic Sites and Monuments Board of Canada under the auspices of the Grande Prairie District Oldtimers' Association.

Presentation of the monument was made by Professor M. H. Long, member of the Historic Sites and Monuments Board of Canada.

Mr. Gordon Albright, son of the pioneer founder of the Experimental Station, performed the unveiling.

A brilliant array of flowers massed to flank the cairn provided a splash of color in the mist-grey setting, heightened by the appearance of an R.C.M.P. honor guard comprised of Cpl. Frank Smith of Beaverlodge and Const. Amos Bramhill of Grande Prairie, in ceremonial scarlet.

As the Beaverlodge Brass Band struck up strains of O Canada and voices of pioneers blended in lusty faith, many hearts bowed in memory of the man who had done so much to help early settlers find security on the northern soil of their choice.

'Although Mr. Albright was a man of vision, he could scarcely have foreseen that the few experimental plots he planted some 40 years ago would develop into this great institution we have here today' said Victor C. Flint, South Peace Historical Society president, as well as friend and neighbor of the early agriculturist. 'This Experimental Farm itself is a monument to his labors.

'It was the problems of the early settlers of this country which provided the incentive for his desire to experiment' Mr. Flint recalled. 'There was no fund of knowledge in those days to guide the settler on what to plant and when. He saw early the advantage of clean fields and new land and his constant message was that this is a land of opportunity and that development carried with it very definite responsibilities. Always he impressed upon us that, as stewards of the soil, we should keep it clean and productive so that we might hand down to our children a goodly heritage.

'In his desire to improve farm conditions he was like a missionary in a new land preaching the gospel of better farming.

'He used his talents as a speaker and a writer to great advantage in promoting better farm conditions. His lectures were greatly appreciated and there is probably no district in the Peace River country where his influence has not been felt.

'He encouraged picnics and gatherings of farmers at the Farm and some of the most successful gatherings of the United Farmers of Alberta were held here at his invitation.

'He had a flair for publicity which appealed to the farming community of this part of Alberta and it is probable that no other Experimental Station in Canada occupied as high a place in the interests and affections of the local farming population as did this one.'

In pointing up Dr. Albright's consideration for animals, Mr. Flint told the assemblage that the practice of unloading livestock in unsheltered, snow-filled corrals to await shipment to market had been discontinued through his efforts.

'Mr. Albright did more to make this country a country of homes than any other single person or set of circumstances could have done,' declared Harry Tuffill, president, Grande Prairie Oldtimers' Association, who served as chairman for the occasion. 'He was an agriculturist and a journalist but he should be called a home-maker as well.'

'Today we have dedicated a monument to one of the great men of this pioneer country,' said William Grant, one of the Peace River Region's oldest settlers.

Robert Cochrane, pioneer, recalled the influx of landseekers 40 years ago and Dr. Albright's unceasing efforts toward helping them build a secure foundation in good farming practices. He recalled also, the stress made on beautifying the rude homesteads and pointed out two oaks on the grounds which had been planted by the experimentalist.

'He took many shrubs and flowers to homes throughout the country and probably did a great deal more good than he was aware of,' Mr. Cochrane said.

In January, 1946, the University of Alberta had honored his work by conferring on him the honorary degree of L.L.D. in recognition of his service to agriculture and his part in the development of the Peace River region.

On the swing of the pendulum in the late Albright era, the town of Grande Prairie had ambitions; some considered it would be good for business to have the Sub-Station relocated on one of the nearby school sections. Mayor Percy J. Tooley provided an alternative in the form of an airport on one of these locations and Grande Prairie will be forever grateful. Then too, the illustrious Herman Trelle coveted a few more laurels and admitted in high places that he had the land, the prestige, and certainly the ability, to take over the Sub-Station.

Fortunately Dr. Albright had staunch friends in agricultural circles, notably Dr. G. B. Sanford, pathologist, who saw to it that reason prevailed.

Perhaps Dr. Albright himself had the last word. Those who worked with him were forever prepared for the unexpected and usually were not disappointed. However, it was a bit of a shock when he penned his own obituary. As he confided to some, who else could do justice to his ambitions?

Under date of March 28, 1946, he wrote:

> This will be the last full installment of 'Timely Hints' to appear under the present writer's name. He retired March 31, 1945, after 30 years' employment in an experimental capacity by the Dominion Government. The cause of retirement is a nervous disorder that has been developing for the past seven or eight years and has reached a point where work is impossible.
>
> The writer has often said that when he retires he hoped to live, not in the city but in the country, puttering around and enjoying the farm home he had helped to develop. This is not to be; one cannot sell his cake and have it too. The pioneer home now belongs to the Experimental Station and residence must be sought elsewhere.

Twenty-eight years ago a young hired man paused to ask 'What is your great ambition in life?' Then, answering himself, he said 'Oh yes, I know. You would like to breed a new, productive wheat of high quality.' Reply came in a moment of inspiration.

'No, you are wrong. That would be a very nice thing to do but its value to the farmer could be easily over-estimated. If it increased the profits of wheat growing it would shove up land rentals until the wheat grower, as a worker, received very little more than before. The original owner of the land would profit and society as a whole might benefit but not, in the long run, the producer of wheat.

'No, there is something I would much rather do than that. I would rather show how good homes could be developed and planted in the Peace, for that is a benefit which would weave itself into the lives and characters of the people, conferring a boon that no economic process can filch away.' I still believe that is true and hope we have done something in the past 30 years to encourage home-making and citizenship in the Canadian West.

Four or five thousand photographs have been taken and 1,000 lantern slides made. Scores of mimeographs have been prepared and thousands of articles penned. Each annual report, whether printed or not, has amounted to a volume. Between 50,000 and 100,000 letters have been written by the staff. Twelve years' records have been kept of 409 lectures delivered in 100 halls and schoolhouses all over the Peace and Athabasca watersheds and beyond. To reach these we have fought rain, mud, snow, frost and divers combinations of these. We have gone a week at a stretch speaking five or six hours a day, fighting the steering wheel by night, retiring on the average about 3 a.m. A week of this is enough at a time, but it was a labor of love! Visitors have been entertained by scores of thousands. The register is adorned with the names of four Governor-Generals, three or four Lieutenant Governors, two or three premiers, two railroad presidents, many statesmen and cabinet ministers, scientists, tourists, land seekers and travellers with addresses spread from Sweden to Hong Kong, not forgetting a Vice-president of the United States. A stack of letters and interviews from oldtimers has been accumulated to enrich the archives of the future.

It is hoped that some good has come of all this work. Sometimes one wonders when he finds his advice ignored or when facts repeatedly published prove unknown to visitors interrogated, or when good established farmers pass from the scene by death or removal. Perhaps one of the great lessons of life is not to take oneself too seriously. Perhaps it is all we can expect if, among much seed scattered, a little finds fertile soil.

Friends of Dr. Albright sought to honor him further. "The W. D. Albright Scholarship Fund" was created to assist deserving Peace River region students to secure further education at the Fairview Agricultural College and the University of Alberta. Thus the Albright influence has been cast on twenty-four students of another generation and has aided them to secure a better education. Perhaps amongst them is a neophyte Agriculturist, Humanist, Protagonist. (See Appendix VI.)

Part II

Dominion Experimental Station

Superintendents:

E. Clifford Stacey, M.Sc.	1947-1962
Arthur A. Guitard, Ph.D.	1962-1965

Research Station
Canada Department of Agriculture

Directors:

Arthur A. Guitard, Ph.D.	1965-1969
Lloyd P. S. Spangelo, Ph.D.	1969-

Beaverlodge, Alberta

TECHNICAL ASSISTANCE

IN 1924 Ottawa officials requested Albright to extend his testing beyond the demonstration stage and suggested techniques which were strange to the Beaverlodge staff. Accordingly he appealed to Dean E. A. Howes at the University of Alberta for assistance. The Dean was known throughout all Alberta for his Irish wit, for his approach to agriculture in the Guelph tradition of service, and for his renditions of Drummond's poetry. For what might pose a problem or crisis to others, he could, by recalling a similar circumstance, find a solution by way of an appropriately philosophical remark.

Clifford Stacey was graduating from university that spring and approached his Dean. "Yes, there is a job at the Beaverlodge Experimental Sub-Station. I don't know much about it but I do know that Superintendent W. D. Albright is doing fine work in a new part of the country. The job carries a challenge and the future will be whatever you make it."

"Beaverlodge? Where's that?"

Two or three Edmonton neighbors had never heard of the place. Another was more knowledgeable; he had heard that it was somewhere in the Peace River region, probably near Grouard. A traveling salesman was more specific: it was near Grande Prairie.

"If you go there, look up Frank Donald. He'll direct you." Frank Donald had indeed become an institution in Grande Prairie. Those who knew him could tell tales of his many pursuits, yet none knew the whole story. By minor and persistent manipulation he had become the leading hotel operator of Grande Prairie, held mail contracts, carried many homesteaders over slack periods and was repaid by labor in his lumber and tie camps. Yes, Frank Donald could direct the newcomer.

Stacey made the mistake of arriving at the Edmonton station of the Edmonton, Dunvegan & British Columbia Railway an hour before train departure. The track was there at 120th Street and 107th Avenue; so was the platform. But the station? A converted box car. Soon a delivery van arrived with cartons of bread. Another drew up with a crate of chickens. Finally another passenger. Eventually the train itself came into sight and to a leisurely stop.

It never mattered whether northern trains arrived or departed on time. Some years later, the porter on the Waterways Branch was said to carry a calendar instead of a timetable and was usually able to predict the day on which the train would arrive at its destination. Stacey's train departed on schedule that day.

Three hours later at Westlock, everyone vacated the train and rushed for the corner restaurant where, to the ring of a handbell, ham and eggs, apple pie, and coffee were thrust at customers. Next morning, in the early hours, the procedure was repeated at McLennan — with the omission of the apple pie. At noon at Spirit River, the habit had become entrenched, with apple pie returned to the menu.

Now what! The train was in reverse! No one else appeared concerned — it must be regular procedure. Things were righted at Rycroft and the train proceeded south to Grande Prairie, having traveled north, west, and now south 401 miles in twenty-five hours. Nowadays passengers jet the 200 air miles in thirty-five minutes.

Beaverlodge was still thirty miles away to the west by dirt road. Superintendent Albright and mechanic Albert Anderson met the traveler. Their vehicle was a 1921 Ford newly acquired on transfer from the Lethbridge Experimental Station where, according to rumor, Superintendent W. H. Fairchild found it could no longer leap the irrigation ditches. Albright had learned to drive en route to meet Stacey and negotiated the return thirty miles in two hours, with various encounters at culverts, square corners, and a few mudholes.

There was much to do and a sixty-hour week was the rule, with plenty of overtime, to bolster Stacey's meager wage of thirty cents per hour. The scientific side of Experimental Farm work was heavily outbalanced by unscientific sweat-and-toil, a fact of life to which young Stacey was introduced on his first day when set to the task of digging in large gateposts; fellow worker Gordon Moyer observed him looking ruefully at blistered hands.

Fortunately Stacey found the work extremely interesting, with old problems continually giving way to new. He returned to university for the winters of 1925-26 and 1926-27 and emerged with an M.Sc. degree, a full-fledged agrologist. His thesis was "An Ecological Study of the Grasslands of the Peace."

First of its kind, the paper attracted considerable interest as more attention was now being given to the Peace. Dr. R. M. Ramp of the Arnold Arboretum, Chicago, used it as a starting point for a similar ecological study in Alaska during construction of the Alaska Highway.

The Sub-Station had become the meeting ground for farm groups anxious for advice concerning accepted agricultural practices. Already the War Veterans' Field Day, an annual event, attracted a large gathering. Superintendent Albright proudly explained the purpose of his trial plots. One year, spokesman E. J. Heller, a Beaverlodge farmer, was pleased to note that vigorous barley varieties were standing at attention, their "bayonets drawn in salute." While Albright painstakingly told of two-row barleys and six-row barleys, Ed Heller indulged in a little research of his own. He checked Albright's barley seedings and reported that they were all twenty-rowed plots!

In midsummer of 1924 there was a special gathering; this time, without the experienced Albright but with the inexperienced Stacey in charge. Sir Henry Thornton, President of the Canadian National Railways, was on a fact-finding tour of the Peace. At the Sub-Station he met every farmer who could leave field work for the day. They were there to request, nay to demand, a Coast outlet.

"Nothing to it," assured Sir Henry. "When production reaches 10,000,000 bushels annually, you shall have it."

Production exceeded that amount three years later. It remained for Premier W. A. C. Bennett of British Columbia to build that transportation link, the P.G.E., (Pacific Great Eastern), into Dawson Creek and Fort St. John in 1958.

Stacey was still a wage-rate employee in 1929 and headquarters at Ottawa was a long way distant. That spring he felt obliged to demand a professional appointment — or else! This was granted and became effective shortly before the stock market crash that November. The appointment as assistant superintendent made the job tenure more positive in the demanding times to come.

The days of World War II were trying ones at the Sub-Station as well as elsewhere. Buildings were badly outmoded and inadequate; staff was at its lowest possible strength. Superintendent Albright was in poor health and there was much to do. By now, as assistant superintendent, Stacey had the able help of agrologist C. Henry Anderson and plotman James Stoker. (See Appendix III.) Somehow experimentation was carried on at the Sub-Station and at many points throughout the Peace. With war's end, Alfred C. Carder returned and within a few years there were a dozen on the technical staff.

In those days, a B.Sc. degree was sufficient to qualify for research at the Sub-Station. But it was evident that a Ph.D. or at least an M.Sc. degree would soon be required to conduct scientific studies in depth. Each in turn took Educational Leave to upgrade his standing. This necessitated endless shifting of responsibilities at work and endless hours of postgraduate study, but ultimately all emerged well-trained and highly valuable scientists.

Again Ottawa was a long way distant. Director E. S. Archibald surveyed the situation and decided that the assistant superintendent would be promoted to full charge, responsibilities he had assumed gradually as Dr. Albright declined in health.

But there was red tape to unroll. "Let us take our time. First we must upgrade the Sub-Station to a Station. Then it will be in order to make the appointment." This took two years, to 1947, to accomplish. By that time, the pay-list teamster, with pressing overtime, frequently was paid more than the officer-in-charge. In later years salary increases and appointments came much easier and in larger gulps.

It was no criticism of Albright to say that the new superintendent inherited a motley collection of buildings and equipment. The homestead days had taught Albright that money did not come easily and that nothing should be thrown away as it would probably find ultimate use. In 1935 he had replaced the straw-roofed barn with a well-designed, Gothic-roofed structure then the mode; but on the meager rental basis he could go no further and obviously Director Archibald was not disposed to enter into a building program without owning the land.

Finally, in 1940 the land was purchased and building began. What headaches! First a site had to be cleared for an office building, but a few fruit trees were in the way. "Desecration!" cried some. Despite complaints the plan progressed.

Finances were difficult. Virtually without blueprints but with one experienced carpenter, a willing staff, and half enough money, a very creditable building program emerged. Later, when it took months to blueprint and longer for Public Works to build, the standard of construction was perhaps one grade higher but cost set the pace for the coming inflation.

Case in point: Arthur Guitard, in charge of cereal breeding, needed six growth chambers for a Ph.D. study and engineered models cost $5,000 each, one costing more than the entire yearly equipment budget. The solution: Half of Jim Stoker's garage was cleared of pipe and other supplies and a few sheets of plywood were scrounged. Within a month the study was under way.

Case in point: Three greenhouses were to be constructed on a slab foundation. Levels indicated an extensive fill. The solution: minor excavation and staff pouring cement for long hours, resulting in valuable basement space for multiple service.

Regardless of frustrations and disappointments, it is readily acknowledged that at all times appropriations were adequate, or at least somewhat in keeping with needs of a developing region. At all times, there was reasonable freedom of action and certainly no political patronage with which to contend.

One problem is recalled: Funds were requested to move the "Harcourt House" to a new location. At the same time, there was a special "rehabilitation vote." Fearful that the house might remain indefinitely, waiting for a building program, the request was duplicated in the usual Public Works estimates. Consternation! Both construction requests were granted! Later, Director Archibald could not think that the house was moved twice but was satisfied when shown that the second vote was used to build a "temporary" machine shed out of odds and ends of lumber, to facilitate the initial distribution of Saunders wheat. The "temporary" structure stood for thirty years but has now been replaced by a modern Butler building. All that was temporary about it were the numerous short-term usages to which it had been put.

DOUBLE DUTY

Dr. ALFRED C. Carder returned from combat duty in World War II only to mount his own campaign of chemical warfare on weeds and insects. With the new herbicides still a relatively unknown tool of agriculture, he found a can of 2,4-D, located a trial patch of perennial sow thistle, and was in business.

Soon an expert on weed control, he took to the highways to acquaint the public with this secret weapon, stopping here and there to destroy the enemy.

The next year District Agriculturists took over this crusade, followed enthusiastically by grateful farmers. Carder introduced most of the new herbicides to the region and has, on occasion, informed weed control conferences that the use of some chemicals as a cure-all in other areas "isn't so" in the Peace.

What was the effect of MCPA, 2, 4, 5-T and TCA and would they control pesty weeds such as lamb's quarter, the mustards, stinkweed and shepherd's purse? Weed workers were becoming organized on a project basis but each had to check controls at homebase to be certain that such herbicides would be effective there.

There remained, however, weeds which showed partial or complete resistance to these herbicides. More sophisticated chemicals and testing methods were adopted and a great deal of time and effort was used to find suitable control methods. Perennial sow thistle was now under control but Canada thistle was on the increase. Field horsetail was the despair of many at High Prairie, toad flax the bane of farmers at Rolla and Codessa, while scentless mayweed had commenced to take over north of Albright.

Dandelions seemed innocuous along the highway, but they reduced grass seed and pasture yields and generally increased cultivation costs. In his wrath, Carder eradicated the weed from his lawn but this was a small success.

On the other hand, wild oats could be spotted readily. If ignored in the field the elevator dockage would be heavy, as high as 50 per cent. The heedless could beat the game; let wild oats shatter in the field and thus save dockage! Grain checks would suggest when the situation was well in hand!

Carder could not agree. He sifted the soil and found as much as twenty-five bushels per acre of wild oats seed awaiting germination. After three years' cropping to Olli barley, designed for control, the soil-borne load was a mere one-and-a-half bushels, still sufficient pollution. The program spelled success.

Carder will agree that the Peace is a "grass" country — if reference is to couch grass. At this writing, eradication is still about as elusive as ever. In 1947 he estimated couch grass had tied up 50,000 acres of the best land and was marching on. A few farmers, such as Fred Labrecque, of Spirit River, a Master Farmer, and Austin Willis, of Beaverlodge, could all but eradicate the weed; others saw small infestations spreading and occasionally taking over entire farms.

At first, reports were that TCA would do the job. However, Carder admits that more than twenty years and over thirty chemicals later, there is really no effective control of couch grass. Robert Holder, Field Supervisor for the County of Grande Prairie, who has co-operated diligently with Carder for many years, would concur. No herbicide has yet been manufactured which can adequately cope with the weed, once it has reached field-scale proportions.

Because of this problem, intense effort was made to find a superior tillage method for control. Much was learned how best to attack couch grass by cultivation but no specific, economic control method has evolved. Tillage procedures are now known which can virtually eliminate couch grass but are impractical because of cost and vulnerability to changing seasonal conditions.

On the front line with other weed fighters in Western Canada, Dr. Carder continues to work closely with the other specialists in this field. At least three important farmers' bulletins: "Chemical Weed Control in Forage Crops, Seeded Hay and Pasture," "Scentless Mayweed Control in Alberta," "Couch Grass

Control in Alberta," published by various agencies, have been written wholly or in part, by him.

Carder also used parasitic insects to control weeds. In 1957 when the toad flax situation at Codessa was grim, a special weevil was brought from the Entomological Laboratory at Belleville, Ontario, to combat it. The weevils were decimated by the first winter or two but a few survived and their acclimated progeny has attacked toad flax with fair success. Thus began a battle of biological control on the Sanoski Brothers' farm at Codessa. Berwyn farmers, across the Peace River, were interested.

Insects have been used to advantage. They have also been fought. Those pesky wireworms, which resemble so much haywire, sometimes take up to ten years to mature.

In the battle against wireworms everyone was patient with professional entomologists. Prof. E. H. Strickland, bent on destroying them, was welcomed by the Beaverlodge Experimental Station each summer, providing him office space in an unused log structure. Lodging in the village was found at The Stopping Place, Mrs. E. A. Smith in charge.

Now Mrs. Smith had her principles and held strictly to them. The "Rules of the House" were posted.

One evening the professor returned from his wireworm research late and was about to retire when suddenly he recalled having discovered evidence of another universal pest — bedbugs — in his log-building office. He must not inflict Mrs. Smith with this insect! Frantically he searched his clothing seam by seam late into the night. The incident was not recorded in official reports. Nor did it leave its mark.

John Mulligan, a Fairview farmer, had neither patience with, nor indeed much faith in, professional entomologists seeking relief from the wireworm problem. No Irishman had to be that patient. So, true to his ancestors, John did something about it. He made his own "cure."

As he was usually short of cash to buy supplies such as food, local storekeepers knew him well. Now they could break even when John came to obtain ingredients for his wireworm "cure" — maybe even make a fast buck. They bought shares in the new enterprise and the money bought the ingredients.

The public bought the stuff and great were its praises. Superintendent Albright and entomologist Kenneth King, of

Saskatoon, sought to investigate. Mulligan declined to reveal the nature of the "cure" but offered a can for trial purposes. Directions called for soaking seed in a mixture of water plus his secret formula for twenty-four hours, then sowing. The treated seed yielded well, almost as much as seed soaked in water alone!

Finally Mulligan became communicative. "What I did was to add everything I could think of to attract the wireworms to the seed then added everything I could think of to repel them." Simple.

The shareholders may have retained their certificates.

Farmers still waited impatiently for victory by the entomologists. Lindane became available and although orthodox entomologists frowned on chemical aids, Carder brushed their objections aside and this proprietary product became widely used. Once when it was unaccountably ineffective as a control, Dr. W. T. Thomas, factory representative of Imperial Chemical Industries, England, manufacturers of the chemical, arrived to protect the good name of their product. With Al Carder and Ken Anderson, of Bear Lake, he learned that the application was made too deep; wireworms worked closer to the surface.

Dr. Thomas also made another observation: Dr. Carder was doing twice the normal research work of a scientist. His weed investigations alone were a full load — and here he was an entomologist!

"Perhaps, said Carder with a smile, "but my prime interest is in the field of agrometeorology."

AGROMETEOROLOGY

Weather records have been tabulated at Beaverlodge continuously since 1913, first on the Paul Flint farm about three miles south of the Research Station and since 1916, at the headquarters site; the latter is situated near the crest of a ridge.

One Sunday afternoon in midwinter of 1925, Cliff Stacey, whiling away the time, chanced to read the weather thermometer situated in the official cage on the Albright lawn. The temperature was a moderate -3 degrees. He questioned, "What is the temperature at the base of the hill?" A second thermometer was carried to the bottom and minutes later, it read -25 degrees. Stacey made tracks for the warmer upper clime.

Superintendent Albright was amazed and interested. In July, 1926, he instituted hillside readings at six points over a distance of 214 rods and an elevation difference of 134 feet. Minimum temperature readings were taken daily for thirteen years. Over this period the average spread was 7 degrees and individual daily spreads amounted to as much as 28 degrees. The explanation is readily understood: The land at the foot of the hill spreads out into a broad slough basin with restricted drainage. In periods of calm, cold air settles just as cold water in a pool settles to the bottom.

The study involved some 5,800 readings and much tabulation. Albright and plotman James Stoker, who did much of the work, reported the findings in *Scientific Agriculture,* November, 1944, and opened the floodgates of correspondence from far afield. It was a major contribution to agrometeorology. However, it was not a new story to homesteaders who had repeatedly suffered frost damage when land clearings amounted to scarcely more than a hole in the bush, confining air currents. Today, the former slough area below the Research Station has been cleared of bush and is much safer from frost incidence.

Explorers and early travelers into the Peace had repeatedly referred to midsummer frosts. Major L. T. Burwash told Albright that he found greater spreads in the Yukon than Albright had at Beaverlodge. On the other hand, John Macoun had read the signs correctly when he noted frost incidence would be alleviated as a result of land clearing. Albright reported that, at the stage of development when his study was made, there was probably a greater spread ecologically between the slough and hilltop, a distance of 214 rods, than between Beaverlodge and Lethbridge, a distance of 380 miles.

While Albright was studying the temperature spreads on the hillside, it was only natural that he noticed the hop vine clinging to the office building. One week it had reached only to the top of the window; the next week it was approaching the eaves. In midsummer the vine was growing as much as 12.5 inches a day. This he would tell visitors who were still not fully sold on the Peace.

Thus the stage was well set for Alfred Carder to study the components of climate and relate them to cropping. But he must have instruments. He needed equipment to measure forces which draw moisture from plants. There were atmometers to record evapotranspiration by measuring loss from a film-like surface, but what model?

At least five were available to Carder but he reasoned that they could not all be "best." He checked filaments, valves, relative efficiency. Such critical scrutiny was scarcely the responsiblity of a one-man unit far from centers of learning. He challenged those already in the field and wrote at least four scientific reports on the subject, implying that most of the equipment then in use was inadequate.

Take snowfall, for instance. The morning message by radio is that four inches fell overnight. To the motorist it means looking for a shovel. The book told Carder that he should record this as moisture, basis ten inches of snow to one inch of rainfall. But Carder had studied at Macdonald College, Ste. Anne, Quebec, and was aware that at times in those parts, snow could be moisture-laden, unlike the flaky fallout of the Prairies. The scientist must first trap the stuff on a board out in the yard or in a funnel. What was the effect of wind eddies set up by nearby objects? Was it cricket to melt the snow? Carder did all this and found that the conversion factor ranged from eight to sixteen inches. What happens when the bright student tells the teacher to rewrite the text? Carder continued to inquire and documented his studies so well that all must listen.

In 1949, Carder commenced his studies, first of their kind in Canada. George Robertson was later appointed to a similar post at Ottawa headquarters and it seemed, for a while, that he was about to swallow Al Carder, but the morsel was all muscle. In due course, other centers of study were established across Canada and agrometeorology developed to full maturity.

Since agrometeorology concerns the effect of weather on plant development, what factors of plant growth are included? What are the components of weather?

Carder studied, researched, analyzed and, at the University of Wisconsin, came away with a Doctor's degree in 1954.

When he returned to Beaverlodge, his first research was to determine to what extent growth and development were affected by the long summer days north of latitude 55. He found that lengthened hours of daylight enabled many common field crops to mature where warmth was limited; also that crops could grow on a low-moisture budget. Thatcher wheat, for instance, was found to produce the same yield at Beaverlodge as at Madison, Wisconsin, with 30 per cent less moisture. Summer moisture and heat may be in short supply in the North but the long summer days make their use more efficient.

Later, work dealt with soil moisture relationships of other common crops. In research it is necessary to know how much water is required to produce a crop of wheat. At what stage of growth does the plant draw most heavily on moisture supplies? From what soil depths do various crops draw moisture? Stock questions to any modern agrometeorologist; pioneering Carder had to find his answers the hard way.

Contemporary with similar studies elsewhere, Carder analyzed the thermoperiod, the effect of temperature on plant growth. Wheat was found to thrive better where days were hot and nights cool. The daily amplitude of temperature fluctuations was about as beneficial as prolonged daylight.

Carder collaborated with William Odynsky of the Alberta Research Council and with the Larry Farstad group of the Vancouver Research Station by contributing to the climatological sections of their comprehensive reports on Peace River soil surveys.

Associated with all this, the climate of the Peace region was analyzed and for the first time, fully described. By 1965 this information was available in bulletin form. A later publication reported on climatic aberrations, notably weather extremes which had occurred at Beaverlodge.

In 1965 Carder and Arnold Hennig, soils specialist, reported that the photoperiod did indeed affect water economy. At Beaverlodge they produced 54 bushels of wheat per acre with only 11.1 inches of water. At Swift Current, 450 miles south, it required 15.9 inches of water to produce 50 bushels, while at Dickinson, North Dakota, 750 miles south, 18.1 inches were needed to produce 36 bushels of wheat.

To the casual observer, the 17.8 inches of precipitation at Beaverlodge may seem scant for satisfactory crop production if he is schooled to high evaporation or to restricted day length. To know the North he must study the North; the Beaverlodge reports are available to him.

FOR THE LAND'S SAKE

To SOME, soil is dirt when dry, mud when wet. To others it is the stuff that produces crops. To the pedologist, soil is a product of parental material, climate, vegetative cover, and time. Physically, soil is the anchor medium of plants.

Fertility is largely a matter of nutrients and moisture, both of which are under the control of man.

When Superintendent Stacey drove a prominent soil specialist from the United States on the Wanham Highway, the latter asked to stop at a suitable road cut, there to read the general precipitation pattern of the region and the nutrient stockpile. The visitor had never before been within 500 miles of the site but, as an expert pedologist, demonstrated the usefulness of science as a tool.

Minutes later on the Watino ferry Stacey drew a cooling drink from the Smoky River, at which the visitor expressed his alarm.

"In the United States, it is unhealthy to drink untreated water!" he declared. Stacey was unconvinced. Surely in Canada, running water was fit for human consumption. That was before he learned that "pollution" and "contamination" were more than textbook terms.

The Peace has been well served by pedologists. Larry Farstad and William Odynsky, with their soil survey crews, have mapped most of the settled areas, while Daws Lindsey has reconnoitered the Alberta frontier by means of the helicopter. All this was a tremendous aid to the Beaverlodge agronomists but it created a plethora of soil series, some sixty-eight in all, with more to come.

To cope with this complex, after much consultation, some fourteen agronomic groups were formulated by Arnold Hennig and Cliff Stacey, about six having immediate economic significance. Then, as an exercise, each group was submitted to a test of recommendations, with the result that the public was advised that there was altogether too much wheat production, need for more land to be seeded to other crops. Dean Fred Bentley, University of Alberta, praised the work highly. Currently, the ARDA (Agricultural Rural Development Act) men will tell of a somewhat similar scaling but they may not know its roots were struck at Beaverlodge.

Soil series are the working tools of the pedologist, since each has basic qualities. Soil families offer a much broader definition but they too have specific connotations. The public has come to adopt some of this terminology but in doing so has created misunderstandings which may cause confusion. Thus it is risky to talk of "Gray Wooded" or "Black" soil without proper understanding. In fact, it invites error to consider any aspect of soil without scientific reference.

Before surveys were undertaken the settler was dependent on his own understanding of the soil, together with the recommendations which could be made by agronomists involved in soil-fertility studies. The surveys did, however, add considerable depth to everyone's knowledge and placed soil understanding on a high level.

To understand any soil it is well to consider its origin. Some is formed directly from the disintegration of bedrock. If the parental material has a high salt content, a hard-pan solonetzic soil will result, especially where precipitation is only moderate as in the Peace. Usually such soil is workable to plow depth but when dry, the subsoil may be relatively impervious to moisture or root penetration and even virtually defy cultivation. Thus it may support a poor crop. Elsewhere in Western Canada there are large tracts of solonetzic soils and Dr. Ross Cairns at the Soils Sub-Station at Vegreville is studying corrective measures.

Most of the Peace River region has been glaciated several times, with ice movements from the Cordilleran region to the west and the Keewatin to the east. The till soils formed from this drift usually occur on ridges and invariably are stony, ranging from gravel strata to the occasional rock which may be dislodged by the plow. Because of their location such soils may be relatively thin and subject to erosion and generally are patchy by reason of their formation.

Fellow to till soils are the alluvial soils, formed by deposits from deposition in water. Obviously these soils are free of rocks and have excellent topography. Picture Lesser Slave Lake once extending through the Central Peace Region to Pouce Coupe, bounded on the south by the Saddle Mountains and on the north by the shoreline at Berwyn. The waters have receded and the deposit has become prime farm land.

Then there are the aeolian soils, formed by wind action frequently piling up sand from lake shores into dune-like formations. They are found for a considerable distance along the Wapiti River south of Grande Prairie.

Definitions could be readily understood if terminated here. But glacial eras have come and gone and each has left its imprint. In places, the simple rules apply; in others, the materials have been reworked time and again, so that pedologists have had to speculate. In the vicinity of Bear Mountain near Dawson Creek, there are several distinct layers of Black soil near the surface, indicating repeated laking and silting. Groundwater studies by the Alberta Research Council tell of an extensive, buried river course below the present Beaverlodge River. The Peace River, for much of its length, has cut through a former lake bed, leaving a channel 800 feet deep and badly eroded banks. Such are the effects of water, ice, and wind.

Now the effect of vegetation. Prairie soils in Western Canada are Brown in color, owing to accumulated decomposition products of grasses. In the deciduous forests to the north, the soil is Black, derived from the well-known leaf mold. Under favorable conditions grasses give way to tree growth in Nature's cycle, hence it must be presumed that wherever grasses do abound, whether in the Palliser Triangle or at Sunset Prairie, the normal vegetative climax has been thwarted. On the short-grass plains, the critical factor is limited precipitation. In the Peace there is usually adequate precipitation but heavy-textured soils may cause precipitation to run off rather than to percolate to storage levels.

Vegetation and the forces which govern it have a further effect. In grasslands the moisture reserves rarely extend two feet downward and thus a surplus of soluble nutrients may be concentrated at this depth. There is, in effect, little movement in the soil, resulting in only a modicum of stratification of the covering blanket.

In tree lands, however, there is usually more precipitation and much less evaporation from the soil surface. Since the subsoil must receive this moisture it is usually porous; water reserves are readily elevated by tree action to the leaf region and evaporated off. The effect is a continuous leaching process which washes chemical components well into the subsoil, leaving an ash-white layer of mineral content covered with a thin mantle of leaf mold. This is a Gray Wooded soil, as named; but try to abandon the term and the confusion it has created and substitute instead the new appellation, Luvisol soil!

Structure adds a third dimension. Obviously sand impedes the movement of water much less than does silt or clay. This influences the retention of moisture in the soil and its ultimate release for crop growth. Most soils store moisture at suitable depths; some light-textured soils by means of a clay strata a foot or more below the surface. Others store moisture readily enough under normal circumstances but take on a bog-like condition temporarily in early spring or in a period of excess moisture, notably the solonetzic soils and the Pineview clay of Prince George, so impervious that the surface moisture evaporates more readily than it penetrates.

A fourth consideration is organic matter. This has involved extensive research at times by Cliff Stacey, Henry Anderson, and Marvin Nyborg and is currently under study at Beaverlodge by Paul Hoyt, Arnold Hennig, and Wendell Rice, with Hoyt spending a year at Rothamsted on the subject. The study continues but the consensus is that organic matter contributes little by way of nutrition, save acting as a medium for the growth of bacteria and the like, essential in the breakdown of crop residues. Structurally, organic matter is very important as it is closely related to the workability of the soil and has a blotter effect in absorbing moisture.

The Beaverlodge groupings and the ARDA classification are good yardsticks and have their place in general evaluation. Most farms are, however, a composite of several soil series. A tillage implement set for conditions at one end of the farm may do poor work at the other end. Some attempt has been made to arrange fields according to contour and soil type; man, however, likes to move in straight lines. Many were the disappointments in pioneer days when a light disc powered by four horses bounced over clods and at times wore down the operator as readily as it reduced the sods. Today, man with his greater power and extremely rugged equipment can rip through the tough spots.

What, then, is fertility? Hoyt and Hennig reason that most of the soil of the Peace River region is amply supplied with most of the nutrients needed for plant growth. If these are carted off as components of a marketable crop there is a renewable supply in the subsoil which can be brought under the influence of moisture and aeration by occasional deep cultivation to restore the loss. Essentially, this leaves the soil experts with one card to play — water.

Fertility, then, is, in effect, moisture rather than organic matter and other considerations. It is commonly known that without adequate water supplies available to the plant, there cannot be normal growth.

Hoyt and Hennig know also that soil type, as such, does not greatly affect fertility and crop growth. They point with pride to many fine crops on Gray Wooded soil and to poor crops at times produced on Black soil. They admit, however, that the Gray Wooded is difficult to hold in proper structure. However, they refuse to refer to them categorically as poorly structured. The Gray Wooded soils which Bert and Spencer Hadland farm are indeed well structured, while some Black soils near Grande Prairie are poorly structured because of high salt content, the result of upward movement from the subsoil. Then, too, there are some sandy soils which normally have no structure whatsoever.

"But," urges the dealer, "we can sell you fertility by the ton and even apply it for you."

"Hah!" ejaculates the oldtimer. "The best individual crops the country ever produced were without the aid of additives."

Hoyt and Hennig would agree with both dealer and old-timer. They have used as much as half a ton of commercial fertilizer per acre in their search for maximum yields, only to produce as much as has been obtained at times without the aid of commercial supplements. They contend that plant growth has a basic nutrient balance requirement and that the nutrient balance in the soil is probably imbalanced for the need. The problem then is to select the crops which most nearly meet the soil's ability to supply and then to supplement the deficiencies by purchase and application. Having thus achieved the required balance, the operator may then consider the economics of applying a further supply of nutrients, keeping in mind other limiting factors such as available moisture.

Nitrogen is most frequently in short supply in the North because it is not generated readily in cool soils. Fortunately a wide range of legumes is adapted which secure and release large amounts of atmospheric nitrogen for subsequent crop use. Thus Albright insisted on a grain-sweet clover rotation for Gray Wooded soils, especially those which had been deep-plowed. Lamoureux Brothers at McLennan owe their prosperity to this practice. Pioneers, whether of yesteryear or those breaking land on today's frontier, have other ways to spend their money than to buy nitrogen, but the choice is theirs.

Phosphorous is the second most important consideration and, as in other parts of Western Canada, it is in relatively poor supply in the soil. Thus it must be purchased but its use should be in balance with other essential plant foods. Its availability, however, is adversely affected by soil acidity. Beaverlodge experiments show that under such circumstances, a generous application of lime would correct this acidity and so enhance the availability of phosphorous within the soil.

There is a distinct problem, a vexing one, regarding acid soils. Most Peace River soils are slightly acid. Larry Farstad and Terry Lord reserved judgment for several years whether they would classify the acid Alcan series as arable. Eventually, with the aid of the Beaverlodge studies, they agreed to it being farmed and crops have been good. Not so in a few pockets, such as portions of the Fourth Creek area where settlers became desperate from repeated crop failure. Ultimately and after extensive study, Hoyt and Hennig found that acidity was induced by the aluminum component of the soils. Now the Alberta and British Columbia soil testing laboratories are alert to recommend the application of limestone to counter high acidity and high aluminum. The expense is much less than the cost of breaking bush land; like breaking, it need not be repeated for a lifetime.

There has been a sniff of sulphur in the air ever since Dr. J. D. Newton of the University of Alberta found at Breton that sulphur was badly needed for crop growth. Dr. Newton followed with a warning that Peace River soils were on the edge of a sulphur deficiency. The Beaverlodge staff, however, could not make a case for it until 1965 when seemingly normal soils over a wide range responded markedly. The circumstances resulted from two previous exceedingly wet summers and it is presumed that the normal supply of soil sulphur had become leached and thus was not readily available for crop use. Now commercial suppliers make sulphur available with nitrogen. It seems that the application of one part sulphur to ten parts nitrogen makes the nitrogen more readily available for crop use.

Visitors ask about boron, knowing that it is an important additive in the Okanagan Valley and at times over a wide belt of irrigation farming. No deficiencies of it were observed until 1965 when under the same circumstances which brought about the sulphur deficiency — high moisture and a soluble plant food — there were a few indications. Thus Beaverlodge cannot say that there is no problem.

There have been occasional complaints that hay yields in the Peace are disappointingly low. Disappointment usually indicates poor management. Picture a somewhat typical Peace River hay field. The sward has been down two years and the silty soil has become compacted, possibly puddled. Flash rains run off and moisture penetrates to storage levels slowly. Thus in midsummer crop production may be in equilibrium with limited available moisture.

Then too, compact soils are cold soils. Under cool soil conditions there is slow release of nutrients from rotting crop residue. Moreover, much of this release is associated with aeration, so that the lack of adequate air in the soil will limit the breakdown of residues.

A further situation is encountered, one which has received very little study and therefore its nature and its effect are not well understood. It is known that decaying processes release gaseous substances such as carbon dioxide, which, in quantity, can be toxic to plant activity. Compacted soils, which impede the inward movement of air, will impede the release of these gaseous substances. The symptoms are stunted, unhealthy growth of poor color despite fertilizer top dressing or other ameliorative practices designed to repair the damage.

Problems may be stated in general terms but correction must apply to specific situations, each of which requires individual attention, be it the soil itself, the puddling action from livestock on wet soil, or the inherent susceptibility of the crop to various levels of toxicity. How else could Cliff Stacey explain a very poor hay yield of alfalfa plots when the yields the year before and the year subsequent were normal? Or explain a very disappointing crop of creeping timothy on the Rowe Harris farm, under conditions which normally produced excellent results? It would take an expert to make an exacting pronouncement; the general agronomist and the farmer must arm themselves with whatever basics they can muster and then apply cool reason.

Thus the story of soil fertility: first Anderson and Stacey as agronomists attempting to cope with a very complex problem; now the newer group of Hoyt, Hennig, and Rice at Beaverlodge together with Superintendents Ken Dawley at Prince George and Ben Siemens at Fort Vermilion, aided by soil surveys, soil testing laboratories, provincial extension staffs, and agri-business personnel working for a common cause.

But progress has been slow and there have been frustrations, such as when Arnold Hennig went out of his way to sample soil for a corporate interest and tests indicated a very low nitrogen content. As a consequence he recommended that barley production should not be considered. Later he looked over the fence and saw nothing but barley — a very poor crop.

Hank Anderson did an outstanding job in studying crop sequence and fertilizer response. He is usually mild-mannered and anxious to get on with his work. But one time his zeal for the Public Interest all but landed him in jail. His test program at Gundy showed a 35 per cent increase in wheat yield from the use of a new proprietary commercial product. Anderson demurred about recommending it and was accused of withholding information. In defense he recorded that a production of 4½ bushels per acre was nothing to get excited about, even though use of the new fertilizer had made a terrific yield increase percentage-wise.

It requires much study before the fertilizer dollar is spent and the public is becoming well informed. The situation is much better than when genial Charlie Moore, of Debolt, was asked by a neighbor how much "Elephant Brand" he should buy that spring. Charlie's reaction was that at least he knew on what level to begin the conversation.

Research does not yet have all the answers to Peace River soil conditions but it has gone a long way in dealing with fundamentals. The ball is now handed to the producer for on-site study and practice.

BEES

The saskatoon is blooming in the hedges;
The apple buds are blushing on the trees;
The apricot and almond paint their bushes;
Ten thousand blooms invite the bees.

—W. D. Albright

MEMORIES of Canadian beekeeping go back half a century, when F. W. L. Sladden was appointed Dominion apiculturist in 1921. Following him was C. B. Gooderham, short of stature and long of devastating wit which could shatter Superintendent Albright with a single word. Charlie was faithful to the Peace. He had, however, one obsession which made him tremble. Bee stings, yes; but mosquito bites would virtually hospitalize him. On his immigration to Canada his mowing machine in Nova Scotia severed a hornet's nest and Charlie was never the same afterward!

Next came Dr. C. A. Jamieson in 1950. All inquiring beekeepers came to know "Jamie" as their friend.

A few colonies of bees were shipped in from Brandon, Manitoba, in 1923. Albright read the book which came with them, as did Cliff Stacey, Johnny Foster, and several others in succeeding years. George Neely's record of 20.5 pounds of daily intake by a hive stacked with many supers, remained for some time. All this was good. It was a way of harvesting fireweed, otherwise known as willow herb, and of pollinating fruits and legumes.

Dr. Jamieson, however, declared the Peace a honey country and predicted 40,000 colonies in the years to come. It was big business in the making. Jamieson was right. In came Jack Smith with 800 colonies. Falher was invaded with honey-hungry Quebecois, many of whom remained and settled in for the long pull.

The statistics: European production averages 35 pounds per colony; Canadian, 75 pounds, and Peace River, 150-200 pounds, depending on the year and the location. The quality: No. 1 water white.

There was only one way to go — ahead.

But Beaverlodge needed an experienced apiculturist, a professional entomologist with an intimate knowledge of legumes. There was one such person — Peter Pankiw. Peter arrived on transfer from Indian Head in 1953. A granary was made fly-proof by tarpaper lining and the new department at the Beaverlodge Experimental Station was in business. And just in time. European foulbrood was taking over in the Smith apiary. Pankiw came to the rescue.

Since then, Peter has been back and forth across the vast expanse of Western Canada, addressing beekeepers' conventions and short courses. It has been an illustrious career. By last count the Peace houses 60,000 colonies. Honey production has amounted to 12,000,000 pounds per year and individual apiaries have averaged 305 pounds per colony, truly a remarkable amount. Daily runs have reached 30 pounds and individual hives have produced 550 pounds of honey.

The source of this production? It starts with pollen from the willow in early spring. Soon comes the dandelion, appreciated by apiarists, whacked at by gardeners, and loathed by farmers when it invades their hay fields. Then come, in rich succession, asters and other native flowers; the expert can identify the source by the flavor. In midsummer, fireweed springs into bloom to brighten the landscape and to fill the hives with the finest nectar. Meantime farmers' fields show an endless expanse of rapeseed and legume bloom.

Beemen have consorted with alfalfa growers but attempts to have honeybees trip and pollinate the flowers have been discouraging. The bees soon tire of the stigma of the alfalfa flower batting them on the side of the head with its spring release, so they settle for collecting the copious nectar without tripping.

Red clover and bees are more compatible. Pollen is freely exchanged but bees do not readily reach the nectar in the corolla tube. Some apiarists shun red clover stands; others claim their best yields from them on occasion. Much depends on the variety and on the weather. Some varieties have very deep corolla tubes; none is rated shallow. Much depends on the apiarist; all have their theories and most regard each other with some degree of deference.

Certain species of bumble bees are able pollinators of alfalfa and red clover and Dr. Gordon Hobbs of the Lethbridge Research Station has developed techniques for their domesticity. Some day this may be the basis of extensive commercial operations. A few are playing the game, but Hobbs is still faced with problems.

With sweet clover, alsike, white clover, and trefoil, there are no problems of honey production and probably no difference in bee preference.

Pollination in small amounts is possible by the action of native bees and other minor insects, but Pankiw has long since proved that an adequate honeybee population, about one hive per acre, will serve to increase seed yields manyfold so that commercial seed production of these crops is virtually uneconomic without the aid of honeybees.

Polish rapeseed requires cross-pollination by wind or bees. Beekeepers have been slow to accept this new crop since it presents management problems, but realize that the acreage is on the increase.

Buckwheat has been introduced but is not well adapted agronomically and the honey is dark. It must be handled separately, else the main crop will be degraded. The production has not been profitable to seed growers and the apiarists have relaxed.

How does the industry operate? An apiarist establishes in a district and places out-apiaries of thirty to fifty colonies. He prefers to have the bees fly half a mile or less to work but knows they will search as far as four or five miles if necessary, in which case their daily input will probably be small. The location is chosen for its extent and variation in bee pasture. One crop species may supply the needed pollen or it might be in full nectar production when its neighbor is suffering from drought or when its flowers are dropping. To the uninitiated it is perplexing to note bees over-flying what appears to be good pasture; the expert accepts the intelligence of the bees to take them where the picking is good.

Thus the apiarist and his bees have a symbiotic interest in the efforts of the legume grower. The only concern of the apiarist is that the growers will seed abundantly and at locations which are readily accessible by truck. The grower, on the other hand, sends out feelers that he will have good pasture and that both will benefit from a large number of colonies nearby. The apiarist might then place a much smaller number there, thus aiming at maximum colony production even if the field is understocked.

In the orchards of California, migratory beekeepers contract pollination as required and then move on, with little regard to honey quality or yield. Some day Peace River seed growers may contract their pollination needs but efforts to date have not been fruitful. The colony-acreage ratio is large and seed growers admit their general need for more pollinators but are slow to act.

Much of this is textbook material, but the story is being learned, although slowly. Pankiw expounds regularly at beekeepers' conventions and at seed growers' meetings. The techniques are well understood and the forces will unite when there is economic need.

The Beaverlodge Research Station apiarist has two able cohorts, Jack Edmunds of the Alberta Department of Agriculture and John Corner of the British Columbia Department of Agriculture. Together they established a joint field day in 1954 and it has remained a stellar attraction ever since, with visitors from northeastern Saskatchewan, southern Alberta and the Okanagan Valley. More than one hundred meet regularly. At least twenty of them operate apiaries of 1,000 to 3,500 colonies.

Jack Smith, of Beaverlodge, Don McCullock, of Fairview, and Charles Paradis, of Girouxville, have won the Alberta Master Beekeepers' Awards. Smith disclaims any success as a beekeeper. He sets out to produce honey.

The Peace River beekeepers do produce honey, 20 per cent of Canada's total production, and truck huge 700-pound barrels of crop to Edmonton and Vancouver for wholesale processing.

Dr. Pankiw insists that for the most part Peace River beekeepers are good technologists. They do their job efficiently and with dispatch. Rapeseed honey granulates readily, hence they now commence extracting in mid-July. This allows them to function with a minimum of equipment, equipment which is clean and relatively free from disease. American and European foulbrood have been rampant but are now controlled by antibiotics.

Overwintering in the Peace has not been economical, even with temperature-controlled storage. Package bees and queens are being trucked each spring from California at considerable expense and effort. This has brought in nosema, a protozoan which attacks the stomach of an adult bee and thus shortens its life. Control is not difficult but requires special management. Pankiw, Corner, and Edmunds have been encouraging overwintering in the Okanagan Valley, and now the Peace derives some 3,000 packages from this source. It is unwise for Canadian producers to be entirely dependent on foreign stocks; there are parasites and diseases which must be avoided.

Other imports show promise. Pankiw has imported queens from New Zealand and is highly pleased. They are gentle and easily handled. The Beaverlodge staff is happy too; no stings have been reported.

Alfalfa seed production is fitful, unless you play the Stan Weston record or recall the excellent yields of Blaine Pierce at Clayhurst, the Jack Ardill production at Farrell Creek, the consistently good record of production at South Wapiti for several years, and the outstanding yield of Everett Short at Taylor for a year or two. Cliff Stacey remembers these well and believes that most of this production could be resumed if a little more research were directed its way and if the growers followed recommendations of the experts. Pankiw begs the growers to check their fields for lygus, a tiny insect which sucks at the base of the flower and thus, when present in considerable numbers, greatly reduces seed set. The growers know the story, but busy themselves otherwise.

Harold McMahon at the Saskatoon Research Station has also been studying alfalfa pollination and finds that if adequate amounts of tree cover are maintained the tiny native leaf-cutter bees will go to work. Quite so at Nipawin, Saskatchewan, and generally throughout the Peace, but in the Lower Peace on the Tony Tretick farm at Lambert Point near Fort Vermilion, there is excellent seed production in the center of a 250-acre alfalfa field and almost none on the flanks. McMahon did not have the answer from his Nipawin experiments but others know that in Tretick's lighter soil, as on the slopes of the Peace River, pollination was done by soil-nesting species. There they are not subject to drowning from flash rains as in heavy soil areas.

Then, too, there have been attempts to establish the alkali and the leaf-cutter bees of Idaho and Washington for alfalfa seed production. Both species have a very short effective flight range and the leaf-cutters are heat-loving.

The Prairie Point Seed Farm of Wayne Wright at Fort Vermilion has barely maintained its stock of leaf-cutters and Hobbs has concluded that the species is limited to southern Alberta. They commence flying when the air temperature reaches 70 degrees, thus are nonactive at most times in the Peace.

Honey production has no pressing problems but attention must not become relaxed in this area of research. Its primary concern is marketing. Legume-seed production, on the other hand, has an expanding market and one major production problem — pollination. The two complement each other and are ably served by Pankiw, Corner, and Edmunds. But the scientific training of these men, together with that of Hobbs and McMahon, must be employed to the limit else a static condition will prevail, to the disadvantage of all.

FORAGE CROPS

SUPERINTENDENT Albright realized that the Peace River region would best be served by a mixed-farming economy. Early in the history of the Sub-Station he set about to formulate recommendations for the use of forage crops. In 1922 he wrote:

> The fundamental importance of forage crops as a means of providing conditions for successful livestock raising and developing therewith a fertility-conserving system of farm husbandry, amply warrants the large amount of attention being concentrated on this line of investigation at Beaverlodge.

The grasses fell into order readily. Brome grass, slender wheat grass and timothy were the favorites. Altaswede red clover was good. Alsike and white clovers were hardy if Scandinavian varieties were used as opposed to Mediterranean sorts. Sweet clover grew well.

But what was wrong with alfalfa? The first seedings came yellow and unproductive. Al Hoover of Beaverlodge had grown alfalfa in Kansas and scoffed that the subsoil was too heavy for root penetration and thus Albright was wasting his time. Then a few dark-green plants were found, then regular green patches and eventually full inoculation. Albright was elated and was soon to astonish field day gatherings with the announcement that unless the plowshare was sharp, alfalfa was hard to kill.

The inoculation problem was solved by Dr. A. G. Lochead, Dominion bacteriologist, sending strains of bacteria, some from England, which were resistant to acid soil conditions. The results were reported by Stacey to the Agricultural Institute of Canada at its 1938 convention in Edmonton and thenceforth commercial inoculation was a mixture of strains.

Later, while on a tour of the Lethbridge district, Stacey was duly impressed by crops on irrigated lands. Dryland farming he knew from boyhood days at Medicine Hat. Only a few fields of alfalfa were noted.

"We know alfalfa is a valuable crop so why not have more of it?" he wanted to know. In defense, the Lethbridge staff reported, "We do sow many acres but root rot kills most varieties after the second year, semi-resistant varieties after three years."

Stacey reflected that some of the Albright seedings of twenty years ago, at Beaverlodge, were still intact. Root rot had been spotted in the Peace but the climate did not favor its spread nor were there irrigation waters to carry the disease. Since then, the Beaver variety has been developed to serve bacterial wilt areas and a shift has been made from nonresistant varieties. Thus Stan Weston, of Fort St. John, promoter of the nonwilt variety Rhizoma, was fighting heavy odds, just as he was when pathologist Dr. William Cormack, on survey for disease, walked into one of his fields, looked around and walked out. Weston of the Golden Hope Seed Farm, so proud of his Rhizoma alfalfa that he charged three prices for the seed, was tense while Cormack made his inspection.

"Nothing there," said Bill with a shrug.

Weston exploded. "What do you mean — 'nothing there'? That's the finest alfalfa known!"

Cormack sensed the problem. Communication. "There is no disease," he clarified.

On the Prairies too, alfalfa has its protagonists. Dr. David Heinricks of the Swift Current Research Station is mild-mannered and unassuming; but when it comes to alfalfa, he is persistent and stubborn. In the most unlikely place for this crop, the driest part of the Palliser Triangle, he bred the creeping rooted variety Rambler and introduced it in 1955. At Swift Current, a single plant of Rambler in a few years can cover several square feet. It has not been easy but Dave has persevered. Now he has developed a new variety, Roamer, which is adaptable further afield and which may find a place in northern pasture programs.

Others are also active. In his doctor of philosophy studies, Peter Pankiw of Beaverlodge found an alfalfa with aberrant floral structure which should have made honeybee pollination feasible, but the bees didn't see it that way. Dr. Carl Lesins of the University of Alberta had had the same experience previously.

Currently sweet clover production is scarcely mentioned unless the price is right or unless the soil needs a boost. Albright referred to it as the homesteader's best friend. The hay crop is difficult to handle but on the homestead it provided a nutritional relief to livestock fed mainly on sheaf oats, particularly as it is rich in calcium. Its principal asset, however, is its ability, along with other legumes, to activate seemingly impoverished soil, whether newly broken or outconditioned by improper husbandry; it adds organic matter which is quickly incorporated into the soil, and its tough tap root penetrates the heavy subsoil which characterizes much of the region, thereby reaching leached layers of plant foods and, on decay, enhancing greater moisture penetration. Unfortunately, overuse leaves the soil fine and fluffy, so that it can scarcely be formed into a good seedbed and is thus highly subject to erosion.

But for a time, sweet clover virtually disappeared, even in such areas as McLennan and Athabasca where formerly it had flourished. Some said the soil was worn out. How could a soil-building crop exhaust the soil? It is easier to believe hearsay than to study the cause; but careful investigation showed that a litle bug had moved in, defoliating the seedlings. Today there is a powder to control the clover weevil.

Alsike grows freely in the Peace, a legacy of seed scattered along homestead trails. It makes scant pasture but its seed crops have financed many a settler's needs. Eventually Dr. Robert Elliott of Beaverlodge studied strains of alsike clover virtually growing wild in places like Prince George and northern Quebec, and developed Aurora, possibly the first truly Canadian variety.

Production of other clovers continues, mostly for seed increase. The Altaswede variety of red clover, developed at the University of Alberta about 1920, has been extremely popular and is regarded by many as a synonym for red clover. However, it is a member of the late Red Swedish group and Europe has many more. Canada, as well as Europe, also has varieties of the Early Red Swedish, or the double-cut group. Eastern Canada harvests the latter early for hay and later for seed. In the Peace it makes only one crop, ten days earlier than Altaswede and lower-yielding. The hay yield is not sufficient for hay purposes but early maturity of the double-cut interests seed producers who dread unsettled weather when the crop is finishing off and who stand to take a heavy loss in threshing a crop not bone-dry.

Northern Europe has a large trade for many fine varieties of red and alsike clovers. Its plant breeders also have concentrated some of the better features, such as leaf retention and plant vigor, into "tetraploids" by doubling the usual number of chromosomes. All these are of special interest to Peace River growers as they offer a valuable market outlet.

However, tetraploids and the normal "diploids" must not become mixed, as the market will accept only pure stocks. Botanically, tetraploids can be crossed on diploids without much loss from sterile seed but the reverse situation can result in loss of two-thirds of the crop, depending on the abundance of each parent, the distance separating nearby stands, and the period of bloom. If the cross does not result in aborted sterile seed, sterility can be detected in the laboratory and thus the Trade will be informed.

The most recent legume seed play is with broadleaf birdsfoot trefoil. To the uninitiated there are several types of trefoil but the market is mainly for this one. As a non-bloat legume, it is highly valuable to the New York Milk Shed and the like. Adaptable to moderate amounts of soil acidity and soil moisture it is important as well to vast areas of Ontario.

As a seed specialty for Peace River growers, broadleaf birdsfoot trefoil has been a headache. The stock seed is costly, establishment is slow, weed control necessary, and shattering losses heavy. However, a few individual yields have been very gratifying, weed control measures are on the way, and experience is being gained. The oldtime varieties, Empire and Viking, may be giving way to the Russian emigrant Leo, Canadianized at Macdonald College. Guelph, the oracle of Ontario production, has come up with Maitland. More will be heard of trefoil in the future.

Creeping red fescue originated on the eastern slopes of the Alps, in the Balkans, and for several years was admired in Canada but not pressed into service. Finally two astute growers, Andrew Anderson, of Innisfail, and John Olson, of Olds, undertook seed production of it. Major H. G. L. Strange, of Fenn, a professional engineer, joined the effort but after one initial success found that he was a better engineer than farmer. E. C. Hallman, of Acadia Valley, was an early seed grower of creeping red fescue and other grasses. Many Edmonton lawns, established thirty years ago, were started with a few square feet of fescue sod purchased from him at one dollar a square foot.

Eventually, James Murray of the Olds School of Agriculture recognized creeping red fescue as a valuable pasture species and entered his Olds variety in the Federal-Provincial Forage

Promotion Policy. This led to Spence Morrison, District Agriculturist, arriving at Beaverlodge in June, 1935, bearing two sacks of grass seed, each weighing about two pounds. One sack contained S-50 timothy, the other Olds creeping red fescue. There had been two bags of fescue and he had left one with Gil Robertson at Brainard.

Now Gil was a splendid fellow. He had helped cut the trail to Pouce Coupe in the early days and was to become a right-of-way purchaser for the Alberta government. But he was not a farmer and nothing came of his fescue. As for the remaining seed, Albright and Stacey exchanged puzzled glances. Albright said he knew something about timothy but what was the other seed? Stacey didn't know either but accepted the challenge.

On July 1, 1935, Stacey conferred about it with Leslie and Rowe Harris, then renting the Stacey farm, and the seed was sown. It was a new, unknown crop; times were difficult during the depression years; mistakes were made, resulting in financial loss for the Harris-Stacey partnership for ten years. Then it began to make sense. Creeping red fescue has since been a steady cash crop for the Peace, averaging more than $1,000,000 a year in revenue.

But its full value has yet to be achieved. Its true forte lies in its ability to produce abundant herbage for pasture in the cooler seasons and to remain green and palatable under the snow blanket throughout the winter. Under good management, its use can greatly extend the open grazing period. Creeping red fescue is truly adapted to northern conditions.

Creeping red fescue is also a valuable species elsewhere. In various parts of the United States, varieties such as Illahee, Pennlawn, and Rainier have been developed for specific needs. Europe has a host of varieties and the Central Farm at Ottawa developed Duraturf. Some of the varieties resemble the fine-leaved Chewings fescue which is rather too sensitive to Peace River conditions to be grown successfully as a seed crop. Currently Dr. Stephen Bonin of Beaverlodge is selecting creeping red fescue for specific turf or pasture use to replace, or as an alternative to, the general-purpose varieties. Picture the time when creeping red fescue comes into its own and Canadian plant breeders and seed growers can offer varieties bred for specific usage!

It was embarrassing for many years for the Beaverlodge Station staff to be asked why seed production of creeping red fescue was confined mainly to the Peace country. The obvious answer was that it was well adapted to the region and that production problems were receiving major attention by the Experimental Station. However, throughout the region such thorough and persistent growers as the Harris Bros. and the Hadlands had their times of disappointment.

One theory was evolved; after years of open autumns and under conditions of favorable nutrition and moisture, creeping red fescue set seed freely next spring. A light-textured soil seemed favorable as it permitted greater moisture and would not trap the poisonous gases of residue reduction.

At the Beaverlodge Station Bob Elliott swung into physiological studies and was soon able to follow the course of bud formation of creeping red fescue and several other species. If conditions were favorable, the buds for next year's crop of fescue were formed in the autumn; even into the winter if the soil remained unfrozen under a mantle of snow.

Conditions in the Peace favor this initiation, just as they do in Washington and Oregon. The process can be enhanced by proper management, including the use of fertilizers. Other species also have their specific period of initiation and this understanding of one of the basic principles of reproduction has greatly enhanced the commercial production of grass seed crops.

But while Elliott researched the problem of how to "turn on" bud development he was also busy in the field. Fescue plants were taken from long-time stands and studied in spaced-plant nurseries. Some plants were short and tufty, others tall but spare of leaf. Think of the variety of shapes and sizes of humans on a bathing beach. In 1966, after study, selection, and purification, Elliott came up with a new variety — Boreal — much more uniform than Olds and at least 10 per cent higher-yielding of forage and seed. In his office is a certificate, "Man of the Year Award," presented to him in 1966 by the Pacific Seedmen's Association as an expression of appreciation shared by the seed trade for his forage breeding and seed research program at Beaverlodge.

Then there is the cousin of creeping red fescue — meadow fescue. Thriving in moist, cool soils, this could be widely grown if it becomes as productive as other species, thus it is waiting in the wings. Hokkin Larson, of Pink Mountain, on the upper reaches of the Halfway River, pastured some 120 head of cattle on one twenty-acre field of meadow fescue from early spring until July the first, with some supplemental grazing on an adjacent hillside, and subsequently harvested four tons of hay per acre from the field that summer. True, an isolated instance under unusual conditions, but meadow fescue reacted at Pink Mountain as it does in central Europe. Who knows how often or where such production can be duplicated in the Peace?

Spence Morrison's other sample, the S-50 timothy, was a creeping rooted type designed for turf purposes and did not fare well at first. Albright grew a good crop of seed in 1936 but there he was stopped. Stacey bought a ton or so of it and with the Harris Bros. designed methods of processing it. A special cleaner was constructed with a Brussels carpet for a belt. The seed was sold in New York State for inclusion in pasture mixtures and production ceased.

In 1962 production of S-50 timothy was resumed as a seed specialty for the export trade, with Harris Bros. and half a dozen neighbors drawing good dividends from a now out-dated Federal-Provincial Forage Promotion Policy.

Hay-type timothy is well known in Western Canada and Albright found it productive in areas of abundant moisture. Studies by Morgan Evans of the United States Department of Agriculture about 1928 clearly demonstrated that this species was particularly sensitive to differences in day length. Now growers the world over can have varieties to their liking, whether for hay or pasture, early heading or late. If England requires a late pasture type which barely sets seeds in that country, the seed trade is alert to have it multiplied. In Canada one school favors an early heading variety such as Champ for one purpose, a late heading variety such as Climax for another; a second school claims that the standard leafy Climax will do for all.

Brome grass was the first grass species to enjoy extensive use in Western Canada and Albright valued it from the start. It is highly productive over a wide spectrum of soil and climatic conditions and may be cropped for hay or pasture. Sod-bound stands are easily renovated. Native to Austria, brome grass stocks in Canada are well established and are classified as "Northern" The "Southern" strains of brome grass are basically more productive but their seed output in Canada has been notoriously low. This situation is being changed with all the rapidity a few specialists, such as Dr. R. P. Knowles of the Research Station at Saskatoon, can generate. "Intermediate" types are now recognized, with ability to produce leafy crops under northern conditions.

Bob Knowles has also been successful in his selection of Northern brome grass. The Carlton 66 variety is fully 15 per cent higher yielding than common brome grass. Thus again, seed stocks must be purchased under varietal name.

Kentucky bluegrass was found to be indigenous to the Peace and, as in many parts of the world, a valuable pasture species where moist conditions prevail. Albright tested it and although he admired its turf he realized that its hay production was low. One season he experienced great difficulty breaking down the sod and reported its "sheepskin" characteristics. This drew an official rebuff that such terminology smacked more of journalism than of science.

Kentucky bluegrass is now selected specifically for rapid establishment, favorable leaf characteristics, and disease resistance, to be used primarily for seeding lawns and golf courses. The knowledgeable, when purchasing their requirements, specify. varieties Merion, Park, Fylking, and the like.

Readers may recall the "instant lawn" of Merion bluegrass which Martin Martiniuk, of Rolla, established on trackside to commemorate the arrival of the Pacific Great Eastern Railroad into Dawson Creek October the second, 1958. Or how his product made the Grey Cup Game after he trucked sod to the Empire Stadium at Vancouver and a field-length strip was laid before the game? By television camera that dark green strip spelled out Peace River sunshine. But the august stadium management is now going all out, with thoughts of using factory turf. Seedsmen should write a letter.

Not to be forgotten is Russian wild rye, which rangemen adore but seedsmen abhor. It is highly palatable but to date most seedlings have failed because of slow establishment.

The late Dr. L. E. Kirk, when at the Forage Crops Laboratory in Saskatoon, made a distinct contribution to Canadian agriculture when he recognized the sterling qualities of crested wheat grass for the drylands. Its ability to persist under conditions of prolonged drought and to respond rapidly to moisture gives cattlemen ample spring pasture and permits stabilization of top-soil in large areas of Western Canada subject to repeated soil drifting. Fortunately, few areas of the Peace are so dry that this grass is needed for hay or pasture. Nevertheless it does produce seed abundantly and could well be an important seed specialty were it not for a somewhat limited demand for seed.

Now another front is developing. Steve Bonin is a relatively new arrival at the Beaverlodge scene, having come from Prince George in 1965 as a consequence of the organization of the Northern Research Group. But he is no stranger to the region nor to the seed trade, having spent three years during the early 1950's buying seed commercially. His work in the Prince George area convinced him that many of the grasses commonly used there were developed for conditions quite different from the heavy clay soils found in central British Columbia; they were for the dry climate and deep fertile soils of the Prairies, the mild, humid climate of the West Coast, or the sub-humid climate and acid soils of Eastern Canada.

He developed an interest in reed canary grass, a native species found on the edge of sloughs, and wrote a doctorate thesis on its inheritance of seed shattering. Here was a grass able to penetrate the heavy Pineview clay of the Prince George district and produce consistently good herbage crops even in dry years. When it is fed quantities of nitrogen, yields become phenomenal.

How to induce farmers to grow it since the seed is expensive and in short supply? Seed growers cannot touch it because one windy day at harvest time could mean nearly total loss of the seed crop from shattering. The answer, of course, is a nonshattering variety. Hopefully this problem will be overcome.

Other grasses have caught Bonin's attention. Meadow foxtail, a little-known grass whose seed is now grown almost exclusively in western Oregon, may become an extremely valuable pasture grass for the North. It rarely goes dormant and its bright green spears seem to push through the snow in spring. It does not winterkill but its light, fluffy seeds are difficult to handle. Bonin is certain this feature can be overcome by mechanical processing to remove the hairy hulls from the seed kernels.

Albright's rotations were slowly accepted by the farming public. Forage seed had to be brought from Regina or Winnipeg at great expense, with the risk of importing weed seeds. In 1928 Dr. L. H. Newman, Dominion cerealist, Superintendent Albright, and Assistant Superintendent Stacey went into committee. The country could grow its own seed. Right. Bill Johnson and Jim Bauman sometimes threshed a few hundred pounds of brome grass and according to reports, a farmer named Christianson, near Grimshaw, grew a little alfalfa seed.

A small clipper-type fanning mill was purchased, with Stacey in charge. A couple of years later the outturn was 100,000 pounds of forage seed. An industry was born.

A few years later W. J. Thompson, manager of the Peace River Seed Growers' Co-op dealing principally in seed oats, inquired if his organization could make money handling grass seed. Stacey replied, "I don't know but at least it would be a good service to your growers."

Who could predict 30,000,000 pounds of Peace River production annually? The signs were there. Robert Cochrane soon afterward produced and cleaned in a homemade mill 90,000 pounds of timothy seed in one year and became known as the largest producer of this seed in the British Empire. Several neighbors were close behind in their production.

By 1962 the seed trade noted that while domestic dealing in forage seed was healthy, there were ominous signs that Europe favored her own varieties and was moving to the exclusion of all others. This became a reality in July, 1962, through the aegis of the European Organization for Economic Co-operation and Development. Superintendent Stacey resigned from the aura of government reports, staff problems, and so forth, to become consultant to this new turn of events. The change in situation was quickly noted by those remaining on the Station. Elliott moved to evaluate the production possibilities of imported varieties, soon to become a major project involving the testing of several hundred varieties from all the principal countries.

Seed production has long since spread from the Beaverlodge Valley into districts such as Whitemud Creek and Kathleen where, during the depression years, scores of repatriated French from Michigan were in desperate straits. The District Agriculturists knew that legumes were needed and assisted them to make extensive seedings of alfalfa, alsike, and red clover. These legumes soon came into production and bins were filled with the seed crop. One winter the Adanac Hotel at Falher was over-run with buyers lining up to offer growers fourteen cents and 20 per cent dockage, or fifteen cents and 18 per cent dockage, or whatever buying pitch they could muster. Horse trader David Harum was never so persuasive! The valuable seed literally poured out of the small fields and prosperity was in its wake.

This production continues. Forgotten are patches of topsoil badly burned by clearing fires, and the vast Donnelly slough bottom which early settlers circumvented. Write the Falher Chamber of Commerce for its success story.

The country is immense; the forage problems are many and unique. Albright, Stacey, Elliott, Bonin, and Pankiw have served well. But where are the others who should be added to the team? For years the call has gone out for resident patholog-ists and entomologists. Once in a while one or the other would arrive, stay overnight and return to Saskatoon, Lethbridge, or Ottawa. Once David A. Arnott came from Kamloops, remained a short time and solved the mystery of the white heads in grass fields. Lately, J. Drew Smith has visited regularly from Saskatoon and has found diseases estimated to cause losses in some years of half the grass seed crop.

It was no joke when Dick Painter, entomologist from Lethbridge, told his ranchers that the grasshoppers ate more grass than the cattle did. When it is known how plants reproduce and what their enemies are, farmers such as David Jamieson, of Rose Prairie, and Aristide Chenard, of Tangent, are fully capable of taking over. Already the Hadlands are producing fescue seed with yields of 1,000 pounds or better per acre and have cropped some fields solely to this species over a period of twenty years. But sometimes these good growers and the Beaverlodge staff wonder what the true potential really is and what losses are being sustained from causes yet to be recognized.

Plant breeding of forage species in Canada has been a hazardous enterprise. There are very few in the game, distances are great, and conditions vary from east to west and from north to south. Try to place a West Coast product on the Prairies. Remember that Ontario's southern tip lies some 450 miles below the 49th parallel, with Windsor as far south as the northern boundary of California and about as far south of Lethbridge as Beaverlodge is north. Or think of the hardy pioneers who came to Falher from the formidable climate of Lac St. Jean, 235 miles north of Montreal but still well below the 49th parallel. The Corporal's Guard of plant breeders are only commencing to satisfy Canada's needs.

In 1952 something was done to give direction to the work and to safeguard valuable varieties then emerging. The Canadian Forage Seeds Project was formulated and those varieties which it adopted were certain of a fair chance of survival.

It was a good move. However, in due time the Project seemed to lose steam. The commercial seed trade whispered that it could provide the necessary punch and invited civil servants to move out. There was talk of Plant Breeders' Rights. One formidable skirmish resulted in the purchase of production rights of one university variety. In 1965 the seed trade had secured access to one half of the seed stocks issued by the Project.

Currently, the odds are even, with the seed trade on one side and the Canadian Seed Growers' Association on the other. Obviously, compromises will be made on both fronts. The Peace River stake is the 30,000,000 pounds of seed produced annually, plus the extra which can be generated, less encroachments of other favored and developing areas such as southern Manitoba.

The seed-trade ploy should be regarded only as a specialized line of production. It offers a cash crop and serves a need for those who feel that they must winter in California or in the local curling rink. But fundamentally seed is used to establish stands for hay or pasture use; thus it is an integral part of the livestock economy. In time, Peace River agriculture will become truly integrated, rather than the present situation where forage is grown essentially for immediate needs.

LIVESTOCK

FREIGHT rates were high in the early days of the settlement and it was necessary that all possible economies be practiced. Some grain producers turned to swine production in an unorganized way; thus the market supply was erratic and the price often disappointing.

Cattle were grazed on undeveloped land in summer and were fed off-quality fodder in winter. Marketing was unorganized and feed supplies badly managed. Too often herds which had been built up over a number of years had to be sacrificed when feed ran low, in spite of Albright's insistence that nearly a year's reserve be maintained. The feed lots east of Rolla were abandoned when grain could be trucked to railhead at Hythe. Fortunately a few breeders maintained their herds and served those who believed in the balanced farm principle.

Many Peace River farmers, after shaking off effects of the disastrous Cow Bill, hoped to recoup with swine production. But what breed?

The American lard breeds were well known, but markets demanded that Canadian bacon be exported to Britain at Danish standards of leanness and at competitive prices. Ottawa's answer appeared to be the new Yorkshire breed, discounted by some as a long, gaunt, race-horse type which made poor gains.

Albright accepted the challenge. He built a series of "Palace Royal" pens into which he placed four pigs each of six breeds — Yorkshire, Berkshire, Poland-China, Duroc-Jersey, Hampshire, and Tamworth. They were fed a scientific ration. Then he called the settlers together in Beaverlodge's Victory Hall to view the carcasses and to go away convinced that Ottawa was right.

The next day the short course was to be repeated at Grande Prairie, with a get-together banquet in the evening featuring talks by H. A. Craig, Deputy Minister of Agriculture, S. G.

Carlyle, Alberta Livestock Commissioner, and George B. Rothwell, Dominion animal husbandman.

The Dominion Livestock Branch at Ottawa sent in F. B. Hanson, a professional promoter. The winner was the Duroc-Jersey, a large, heavy-larded enemy. It was disastrous. The show must be stopped!

"No," declared Albright. "We shall tell the truth."

The truth was that while the Yorkshires came second best when one formula was applied, there was a variation within them which pointed to a winner if rigid selection were practiced within the breed. It was a serious strain of Albright's principles and those who worked with him later would remember it when skies turned gray.

The Yorks eventually became a hardy, robust breed. The famous Prince Edward Island strain, able to produce a good carcass, was unable to withstand rigorous winters until taken in hand by breeders in the West.

Sometime later, Albright's pigs were ailing.

"What causes swine to walk in circles and have difficulty lying down or rising?" Beaverlodge staff wanted to know. The pens were full of symptoms and Albright was worried. Case histories went out by dozens and replies, intended to be helpful, were useless.

Headquarters sagely advised a little freshly ground wheat be added to the ration: The case histories had listed wheat in the ration. Dean Sinclair of the University of Alberta told of research at Edinburgh indicating weak litters from insufficient vitamin A. The Albright letters were precise: Pigs did not weaken until well grown.

Stacey, convinced that somehow vitamin A was involved, reread the Sinclair letters. Albright added fresh alfalfa hay and pilchardine to the ration and in a day or two the pigs were romping. Once understood, the trouble could be invoked or corrected at will. It is elementary now, that body supplies of vitamin A will become depleted if the supply is not maintained, especially in northern latitudes with a relatively long feeding period. But in 1938 it seemed that no one could help Albright regardless of voluminous case histories.

A herd of registered Shorthorn cattle was established, but policy dictated that the choice of breeding stock could be made only by officials from headquarters. Two from here, three from there, and so on. The five heifers from Scott may have had pedigrees stretching from there to Beaverlodge but were culled shortly after their arrival. The highly touted bull of Irish breeding from Brandon was to be a "find." He lasted one year and his progeny scarcely more.

Livestock assistants Bruce Owen, A. R. (Jerry) Jones, and Arthur Reddon strove diligently but the cards were stacked. Owen went on staff of the university at Saskatoon, Jones to Farm Business Studies, Alberta Department of Agriculture, and Reddon became the swine specialist of the Alberta department. Fundamentalists at headquarters demanded studies to encompass the entire domestic composition of the herd, while those on the scene preferred to secure the stock needed at the time from commercial sources, financed by a convenient revolving fund.

As usual, Ottawa admitted "local autonomy" but maintained final authority. The procedure was to request a long-term plan for committee consideration at headquarters; before this could be instituted a call would come for another long-term plan for the Station. At Stage 4, Jerry Jones went into orbit.

Eventually a creditable herd of cattle was built up at the Beaverlodge Station but it was liquidated in 1966 when Ottawa was finally convinced that the real need at Beaverlodge was studies in forage utilization rather than in basic nutrition or in genetics. A revolving fund would supply test animals when they were needed, thereby relieving the budget of responsibility of year-round maintenance costs.

Regardless of difficulties, some important studies were conducted. At one time swine raisers in the district suffered severe losses from enteritis and the Station was besieged with requests for aid. Investigation revealed that finely ground oats contained numerous needle-sharp splinters which could readily pierce the intestines. This could be avoided by coarse grinding or rolling. Some brands of commercial feeds likewise contained these sharp splinters but management declined to alter the processes since it would add to the cost. Another cause of enteritis resulted from unsatisfactory sanitation, which was corrected when the corners of the feed troughs were scrubbed out and the hog-house washed down. The hexagonal farrowing house which had become popular had innumerable corners to clean and was considered by some to be a primary source of infection to new-born pigs.

Later the use of farrowing crates was advocated throughout Western Canada but handling experience was essential for satisfactory results. This received considerable attention at Beaverlodge and the industry benefited; but work of this kind does not readily enhance professional advancement nor does it make a strong case for budget demands.

But strive the staff did. Art Reddon was in the front line of changing attitudes towards cattle returns when he used the breeding herd for two winters in a study which showed that straw plus threshed grain could well substitute for high-quality hay. In some feedlots this thought has been developed further and advanced stages of feeding consist almost entirely of grain.

Likewise, Reddon studied the occurrence of ridglings in boars and sought to determine if it was a hereditary trait, which it proved to be. Dr. J. A. Newman of the Lacombe Experimental Farm became involved in the work and concluded the experiment, with work being carried on at Beaverlodge by technician George Dawson after Reddon's departure.

At the Fairview Agricultural College, animal husbandry instructor Don McPherson thought to warm the drinking water for milk cows and they reciprocated with a better milk flow. Settlers paid attention and were reminded that livestock required more attention than merely being provided with shelter and fodder.

Trevor Jones, McPherson's successor, finds teaching lads from the farm, eager to question, a challenge. Trevor, raised on a cattle ranch, had come to like sheep. He imported Finnish twinning rams to increase the lamb crop at the college and he is now self-feeding ewes and is feeding lambs on raised platforms which allow four square feet for each to turn in. He reasons that by this confinement and by pushbutton control, he needs to give the pens only a few minutes' attention each week. Space a little larger than a two-car garage devoted thus would keep the farm family in groceries all year. Trevor says that his students have the message.

There has been criticism at times in regard to stocking the Peace. Demonstration was fully justified in pioneer days as it was close to the settlers' needs, and the progeny was available for upgrading local herds. This did occur at Beaverlodge, involving cattle, horses, and sheep; at Fort Vermilion, with cattle and horses; and at Mile 1019, involving cattle and poultry. But livestock research is very demanding and the Beaverlodge staff could not outline problems specifically unique to the region, problems which could as well be investigated at centers of major concentration such as Lacombe and Brandon. The possible exception was Albright with his vitamin A studies, which he encountered rather than initiated.

A different situation existed at the Prince George Experimental Farm. Abundant feed supplies and the need for local milk production justified the establishment of large herds of Holsteins and Ayrshires. This became a component of the detailed, co-operative study, involving several Research Stations, of the genetics of production and the influence of environment. Presumably valuable data were obtained; regardless, the Prince George herd was dispersed in 1969.

Thus despite earnest attempts at Beaverlodge and Prince George, together with exploratory trials at Fort Vermilion and Mile 1019, research investigations pertaining directly to livestock were discontinued as a matter of policy in favor of this work being done at a few Experimental Stations duly staffed and equipped for such research. Nevertheless it was maintained that livestock did have a place in northern agriculture and its function should be essentially that of feed utilization.

PASTURES

AFTER much hesitation at Ottawa headquarters, a "Pasture" assistant was appointed to the Beaverlodge staff in 1950, in the person of Martin Martiniuk. This step happened to coincide with heavy bush fires in the Canadian North, causing severe loss of timber and topsoil over hundreds of square miles, the smoke of which darkened the sky as far away as New York City and 200 miles beyond.

Martiniuk set out to make repairs by scattering seed in the ash and amongst the brush, obtaining strong stands of most species. The legumes persisted but the grasses quickly ran short of nitrogen.

Ottawa was puzzled: Martiniuk had not bothered to clear the brule. Instead he had reasoned that cattle could walk over deadfall to get at feed for the taking and that the money would be better spent on extending his pastures. At Mile 25 on the Alaska Highway the experiment terminated after a woodcutter chose to pasture his team of horses on the bush pasture, the only growth for miles around.

What once seemed utter desolation in the path of fire at Mile 25 is today the $1,000,000 South Peace Stock Farm.

Oldtimers will recall the round sheep barn on the R. A. Hill farm en route to Pouce Coupe. Hill was a long-headed homesteader who made a living with sheep and a Fordson tractor, despite the fact that the soil was Gray Wooded, the tractor inadequate, and marauding coyotes lurked in the bush. His pastures were always depleted near the buildings and if hungry sheep ventured afield, the least disturbance stampeded them home.

Martiniuk was ambitious and resourceful. On the Hill farm he plowed the land well and seeded it to plots without thought of failure. At the same time he secured on loan twenty head of Hill's sheep, culls of the flock, for a small dietary trial at the Beaverlodge Station. Their owner could scarcely recognize his well-fleshed property on their return.

The Hill operation was quite different from the orderly procedures on an Experimental Farm. For one thing the work crews ate at "Ma" Brainard's famous stopping place. On one occasion Superintendent Stacey showed Director General Robert Glen the experiments and the two had supper with the rest. The visitor was duly impressed on both counts.

"When you get back to Ottawa," said Stacey, "tell the audit department that the Brainard meals are one dollar, and eat as much as you like. The accountants won't take our word that there is one price only. Why, last week a party of American tourists thrust extra money at Mrs. Brainard and were all but thrown out!"

The meal was good. Mrs. Brainard gave Stacey a jar of her famous crabapple jelly and a Martha Washington geranium for his wife and would not accept payment for the two meals.

"I don't understand," protested Dr. Glen.

"Don't try too hard," counseled Stacey, "or I may have to tell you that Mrs. Brainard sent word last spring she was out of chicken feed. Sometimes we break departmental regulations."

"There are some things Ottawa doesn't want to know," Glen replied.

The plots on the Hill place thrived, so did the sheep — and so did the coyotes. Mr. Hill was amazed at the productivity of his land when it was well farmed. Under county supervision, Martiniuk baited a carcass with the new "1080" and rid the area of coyotes, also sheep-killing dogs from the nearby Indian reserve. Arthur Wilson, Alberta Field Crops Commissioner, rated these trials the outstanding experiment of the decade.

In 1957 M. F. Keeping, of Demmitt, presented his problem: How could he establish pasture for his milk herd without going to the trouble and expense of breaking the land, picking roots, and so on, where standard treatment was all but impossible because of many rocks? Jack Dobb of the Beaverlodge staff responded and did the obvious — scattered seed following bush removal and lightly worked it in. The result: normal crops of a brome-fescue-alfalfa mixture.

Keith Murray of the Grazing Division, British Columbia Department of Lands and Forests, heard about this seeding. Later Dobb and Murray's successor, Douglas MacLennan, went to work at Groundbirch and Sunrise Valley and in a very short time several community pastures were established. Thus the stage is set for similar development of 13,000,000 acres of marginal land in the Peace, when the world becomes sufficiently hungry.

When Jack Dobb resigned in 1964 to go farming, William Pringle, fresh from a stint with F.A.O. in Turkey, took charge. Bill had done outstanding work amongst the high-line ranchers out of Kamloops and was conditioned to bush pastures. He continues to work with Doug MacLennan and the team has established basic procedures. Outdated is the partial preparation of the Keeping trick because of difficulties with regrowth and the like, in favor of better control and higher yields, gained from cropping cereals for three years, then seeding down and fertilizing.

Dr. Herman Vaartnou came to aid Pringle. Although he remained at Beaverlodge only slightly more than a year, he made an extensive collection of potential forage plants throughout the North which, with additions by Pringle, amounts to 3,200 individual plants in the Research Station nursery.

In 1930 during his trip north, Albright was told of the Slave River lowlands and he photographed huge stacks of wild hay harvested from them. Dr. John Day, federal soil surveyor, estimates this block contains 1,700,000 acres of pasture land and some have conjectured that it could feed 300,000 head of cattle. Pringle and Ben Siemens, Superintendent of the Fort Vermilion Experimental Farm, are currently engaged in a project to determine the true potential.

The Grazing Division of the British Columbia Department of Lands and Forests, active in the Peace River Block, has set aside 700,000 acres for grazing and other Crown usage. Eleven community pastures have been established and their development is in full swing. The highly complementary objective is a thoroughly integrated use of Crown land involving grazing, forestry, recreation, and wildlife.

On the Alberta side, some 43,000 acres have been designated grazing reserves, with an additional 150,000 acres leased to twenty-five grazing associations.

Doug MacLennan has tested many pasture species, alone and in combinations, and finds the mixture of creeping red fescue at four pounds per acre and alsike at five pounds, superior to all others for holding pastures. In general use he recommends a mixture of timothy, creeping red fescue, alsike, and alfalfa, sown at ten pounds per acre. He prefers a turf species seeded not too thinly and not too thickly; one which is hardy, makes early spring growth, withstands trampling, and produces abundant fall growth which does not freeze down when winter comes. All these attributes he finds in creeping red fescue. Timothy makes excellent summer pasture, particularly in low-lying areas. The alsike is added for what it contributes directly to nutrition. Indirectly it supplies nitrogen to feed the grasses.

Present indications are that under reasonably favorable conditions Doug's pastures will carry a cow and calf on two acres during the summer grazing period, with a 25 per cent residue against overgrazing.

With good pasturage available, it is a paradox that there are very few genuine ranches in the Peace River region. Most of the livestock are carried as a component of a mixed-farming enterprise. Some farmers have rushed into raising livestock, blundered badly and met disaster before they learned. Grain farmers can suffer disaster and bounce back. Cattlemen need time and money. But the feed is there for the taking.

Harry Hargrave, director of community pastures for the Prairie Farm Rehabilitation Act, was stunned when he stood knee-deep in Peace region grass and couldn't see a cattle beast for miles. Only recently has Doug MacLennan been able to advise with confidence. Bill Pringle and Trevor Jones have their programs scarcely under way and know there is much to be done. Not only have Peace River cattlemen refused to listen but they have not fully assessed their position, become vocal. Short-grass ranchers have dominated their scene. Dr. William White, then at the Federal Forage Crops Laboratory, Saskatoon, in staff conference quite a few years ago, issued the challenge that there were more cattle on farm pastures than on ranches.

The basics are available to the stockman; refinements will come from research, management, and experience.

When pressed for the reason so few cattle are raised in the Peace the classic answer is that summer pasture is short, winter feeding period long and rigorous.

"Not so," argue Montana cattlemen. "Winters may be long;

extra feed will compensate for that. But your winters are not that severe. Did you ever experience a Montana blizzard?"

Whether or not by intent, J. B. Early set the Peace River cattle pattern with his splendid herd of well-bred Jerseys which roamed the hills of the Peace and wintered in an open-front shed.

"Can't be," declared the fieldman of the Jersey Breed Association. "The animals would freeze to death."

But they thrived. Cattle do not need closed and heated barns and stanchions. Give them reasonable shelter from wind, dry backs and a warm manure pack to rest on and they will be content.

As for the short summer pasture concept, this is a product of mismanagement over the years, when pasture was rough land stocked to overflowing with bawling cattle. Well-established pastures were badly managed. Good land was too valuable for feeding cattle. Indeed it was, under the poor pasture regimes to which it was subjected.

Horses can be readily pastured on creeping red fescue aftermath all winter and thrive. Cattle can do the same, snow conditions permitting. Given proper understanding of the species, plus good management, cattle can be grazed nine, ten, or eleven months a year. Skeptics will have to be convinced but this is presently being done in isolated cases. Shelter need only be minimal; silage or stack reserves will supply in off-season.

The Peace River breed of ranchers has still to appear but when they do they will find a haven.

If Beaverlodge had been more active in its livestock programs, perhaps more livestock might have been raised on Peace River region farms, although this is doubtful since Alberta and British Columbia Departments of Agriculture, livestock divisions, have served the country well. Perhaps, with more emphasis on livestock, other fruitful lines of study might have suffered. Perhaps Trevor Jones and the Agricultural and Vocational College at Fairview more positively meet the need, thus are justified in conducting their demonstrations and exploratory programs. At least it can be said that the College's work is injecting a concern for livestock into the minds of a younger generation and supporting it with locally obtained data.

Why should only 5 per cent of Canadian hogs be marketed

from the Alberta sector of the Peace and perhaps a relatively lesser amount from the British Columbia sector? Why should as much as 95 per cent of Peace River cattle arriving at the Edmonton market grade "unfinished"? Why has sheep production almost disappeared? All this, in a land of high transportation costs and ample feed?

There is no question of the productivity of the Peace and of the North beyond. Can it be that the true economy of the Peace will be achieved with a predominantly livestock program? If so, it will find competition in the major feedlots being established to the south. There is no second handling of swine and probably not of sheep, but there are several stages of cattle production — cow-calf, feeder, and finishing. To which is the Peace primarily adapted?

Peace River farmers continue to flirt with cereal production, while ranchmen are moving in, slowly. Livestock must have a key place, but a variety of circumstances hardened the pioneers against it. The new generation is more favorably inclined.

The attitude of the Beaverlodge Research Station is that a major contribution is overdue in the matter of feed utilization and to this end, it is committed.

CEREALS

HISTORIANS have recorded repeated disastrous attempts of wheat production by the early settlers of southern Manitoba. What, then, might be expected of a region 1,000 miles away, to the west and north?

It would be logical to expect that the North might have to wait a long time for production but in 1875 Professor John Macoun saw fine wheat and barley grown by the Oblate Fathers at Fort Chipewyan. He took samples with him and had them entered at the Centennial Exhibition in Philadelphia in 1876, where they were awarded the Bronze Medal.

Then in 1892 Rev. J. Gough Brick was growing wheat at his mission settlement at Shaftesbury and his son, Fred, recalls that his brother Allie, then twenty-five years old, prepared a show sample of it by pouring the wheat out of an upstairs window so that the chaff and light-weight kernels would be blown away and the heavier grain would be collected on a blanket. There was no hand picking and no hand polishing. The sample weighed seventy-two pounds per bushel. Thus the story of the World Champion wheat entry at the Chicago World's Fair in 1893.

But this was not the earliest grain production in the Peace. Trader Daniel Williams Harmon reported in 1809, four years after Fort Dunvegan had been built by the North West Company, "We have cut down our barley and I think it the finest that I ever saw in any country." At Fort Vermilion the Hudson's Bay Company had established a post in 1802 and in 1876 Bishop Bompas of the Anglican Church sent in Rev. A. C. Garrioch to establish a mission and an Indian Industrial School. The farm operated by this school was probably the first field-scale enterprise in the Peace. Later the H. B. Co. and Sheridan Lawrence were to establish flour mills at Fort Vermilion to supply the needs of the territory — Fort St. John through to Fort Simpson. When the E.D. & B.C. railroad reached Peace River Landing in 1915, Sheridan Lawrence had seven carloads of wheat, mostly Number 2 Northern, moved upstream for shipment to export markets.

In 1907 James Mead, of Lake Saskatoon, imported a few sacks of Kansas Red (Turkey Red) winter wheat from southern Alberta and for several years had it grown under contract by neighbors. This was the source of Albright's stock of Turkey Red, a variety which rated limited winter hardiness in Kansas. It is probable that its hardiness improved as the result of repeated seedings in the North as present stocks are about as hardy as the hardiest, Kharkov 22. Amos Sherk, of the Bull Outfit, introduced the variety Dawson Golden Chaff, which he had grown in Ontario, but soon discarded it as it lacked hardiness.

In 1908 or 1909 Jim Mead, then in partnership with William Grant, introduced Red Fife spring wheat, at a freight cost of eight cents per pound, but the shipment did not arrive until June. But seed it they did and surprisingly the crop matured and yielded forty bushels per acre. Subsequently it continued to yield well but was subject to smut infection and ultimately was replaced by the earlier maturing Marquis, a variety now considered much too late for safe cropping save on the breaks along the Peace River. Thus the story of Peace River's wheat production prior to the Albright era.

Ruby was one of the finest wheat varieties bred by Dr. Charles Saunders. It matured very early, hence it was in Superintendent Albright's plots back in 1916. The report said that he lost considerable part of the crop from shattering.

"Couldn't be!" refuted Saunders. "No one else has reported shattering in Ruby."

But Albright in his simple program had found something vital that others were soon to experience.

The Russian variety Ladoga yielded exceptionally well but Albright knew that its bread-making qualities were highly objectionable. He had his work cut out to find a suitable variety.

Assistant Superintendent Stacey, as a cerealist, was encouraged to experiment by breeding or selection. He tried valiantly and on two or three occasions seemed to make a breakthrough, at least insofar as Beaverlodge was concerned. But the Quality Boys and the Pathologists had their say, as was proper, and that word was disheartening. The team was yet to be organized and the individual could not cope with all the demands.

Disheartening, too, was the experience of Albright in 1928 when he learned that plant pathologists, like entomologists, were a race apart. They just did not think like other human beings. Dr. Margaret Newton, at the peak of her fame for work in the Dominion Rust Research Laboratory in Winnipeg, had reached Beaverlodge on a stem rust survey. Obviously she was too far afield, but as a true scientist, she must comb the wheat plots for infection.

"I got it! I got it! This is an historical moment!" she cried in triumph from amidst the plots.

"Got what?" the startled Albright wanted to know.

"I have found rust this far north and west — for the first time!" She was elated. Stem rust had been found on late-maturing plants.

Albright did not share her enthusiasm. He had enough troubles without the plague of stem rust of the Prairies bearing down upon him! He was consoled, however, when reassured it would take several weeks for the rust spores to spread from the north-central States and the wind currents had to be right. By that time, Peace River wheat would be sufficiently mature to be unaffected.

None has denied the need for rust resistance in grain for the Prairies, but regardless of the fine efforts of experts such as Goulden, Peterson, and Johnson, the effectiveness of the Winnipeg-bred varieties of wheat rapidly diminishes westward into Saskatchewan and was barely noticed in the Peace.

In Stacey's dawn as a cerealist, there were two wheat finds: Garnet and Reward. Both matured quickly, thus they were right for the Peace. Garnet could be harvested early and maintained its excellent color; Reward yielded a little less, but had first-rate bread-making qualities and was in special demand for show samples. Garnet was descended from the infamous Ladoga, which along with all its progeny, was subject to degrading. It is still in fair demand as many regard it as the best wheat variety for the North.

Reward wheat truly made a striking sample and was the principal variety used by world-famous Herman Trelle, of the Lake Saskatoon district.

Trelle, who first focused the attention of the world on the Peace River country's ability to produce wheat, had left the University of Alberta on the completion of three years of engineering, to farm with his father at Lake Saskatoon. A P. T. Barnum as well as an excellent farmer, Trelle soon flooded the Toronto Royal and Chicago International Hay and Grain shows with samples which were destined to be labeled champion exhibits. He collected some 135 champion awards in about ten years' time and his helpers, the equivalent of today's 4-H youths, Lloyd and Justyn Rigby, Peter and Paul Sebastian, and Douglas Clarkson, took almost as many more.

Trelle was no shrinking violet. He returned at one time from receiving more laurels at Toronto and descending the steps of the E.D. & B.C. Railway coach, looked up and down a deserted Wembley platform and demanded, "Where is the band to meet me?"

On another occasion, he went into Edmonton and came out with a buffalo coat, a grand piano, and other booty, presumably gifts of appreciation.

Trelle once boasted to University of Alberta's Dean Howes that he could talk in ten languages. The somewhat sardonic dean commented, "You know, Herman, you should learn to keep quiet in ten languages."

Trelle was likable and his success and showmanship brought literally thousands of settlers to the Peace. In 1936 he was commissioned by the Associated Boards of Trade of the Peace River to prepare an exhibit for Vancouver's Golden Jubilee, and on his departure he admitted to the press, "Never before was there such an assembly of grains and grass seeds as that which will represent the north country." On his return he reported to an appreciative audience in Speke Hall, Grande Prairie, "The super grand excellence of the superb quality of my grain left them speechless." Trelle was never left speechless.

Quick to capitalize on success, he multiplied his stocks of Reward and had seed to sell. It had to be good for commercial use — had not it taken several world championships? Dr. A. G. McCalla, a university biochemist, would not admit that Trelle's Reward or any other wheat from the Peace should be allowed to degrade Canada's export stream. But Trelle was not dissuaded, he never did anything by halves. His Reward was ballyhooed as Wonder Wheat. It was his own selection of Reward, but he never convinced a cerealist that it was wonderful beyond all reason. The price: twenty dollars a bushel for well-cleaned seed plus the Trelle smile — if you were a stranger. Neighbors got the seed at five dollars but no smile.

Barnum was right. There's one born every minute.

In the spring of 1941 Carl Fraser and Fred Gfeller of the Cereal Division at Ottawa sent along several selections of a new hybrid designated C-26-44.7. Walter Johnston, starting his career as a barley breeder at Brandon, could add a few selections from the same cross. Testing at Beaverlodge went into high gear. Soon the search narrowed to three selections, the making of a true Peace River wheat variety. By 1946 Dr. L. H. Newman, Dominion cerealist, was impressed but asked that the variety be tested further.

But how? Labor was scarce in 1946 and Hank Anderson and Cliff Stacey were carrying the full responsibility of administration and research for the whole Beaverlodge Experimental Station. But there must be no stopping. The map was spread out and thirty-five growers of known reliability were selected. A letter was sent by way of explanation and everyone responded enthusiastically. Anderson and Jim Stoker started off in all directions, seeding a block of plots at each location and later harvesting the crop.

The results were examined for reliability by Dr. Cyril H. Goulden of the Rust Research Laboratory at Winnipeg and were pronounced excellent, a rare compliment. The Plant Breeders' Committee of the National Research Council was duly impressed but conservative.

"Do it all over again, just to be sure!"

So Stacey, Anderson, and associates went back to work, with equally good results. The variety was now accepted and fourteen lots of seed plots were multiplied over winter in California, then a new means of expediting increases. Further increase was made the next summer at Beaverlodge on the farms of neighboring seed growers. It was a trying time for the war-shortened Beaverlodge staff, but the spirit of co-operation such as existed between the growers and the station made the work easy.

The new wheat was named Saunders in 1947, in memory

of Dr. Charles Saunders, breeder of Marquis and many fine-quality wheats which did so much to make wheat growing on the Prairies possible. But now the emphasis was on the North and it was hoped that the new variety would extend wheat production northward and so expand the Saunders' influence.

Reference to testing recalls to mind a ridiculous incident. A Chicago laboratory was making a study of bread wheat from selected regions and asked Superintendent Stacey if he would oblige by sending a bushel of Peace River wheat, Thatcher variety. It would be a pleasure, he replied, and the shipment was dispatched, carrying charges collect but no commodity billing in favor of the Receiver General of Canada.

A month later word was received expressing the regrets of the Customs Office, Emerson, Manitoba, that export to the United States of America could not be effected as the current Canadian quota of 30,000,000 bushels had been filled. In no way could Stacey's one bushel be squeezed in.

Stacey replied that no commercial value was involved; the wheat was for laboratory purposes only and had been sent at the request of the United States agencies. Thus there was nothing that he could do about it. Another month later the Northern Alberta Railway's agent at Beaverlodge explained categorically that demurrage charges were mounting and the wheat would have to be sold to compensate the railway for its services. The next day from N.A.R. headquarters in Edmonton a very irate department manager demanded to know what Stacey was going to do about it. Stacey replied that he could do nothing more and referred all and sundry to the Chicago Laboratory.

So much for international involvement!

Peace River producers recognize that prairie wheat sets the pattern of the export stream, but are also aware that they, too, can contribute fairly. At times the Hard Red Spring grade has flowed from Fort Vermilion and from the breaks of the Peace south of Berwyn and Fairview. Nevertheless, a large percentage of the crop does not make milling grades, although in one year, samples grown in plots at Beaverlodge, where the Station residences now stand, rated highest in protein of a Uniform Variety test conducted at all experimental farms and universities in the Prairie Provinces.

Earlier, in 1925, Professor T. J. Harrison, then at the

University of Manitoba, undertook a survey of the quality of wheat grown in various parts of Western Canada. The seed arrived at Beaverlodge late and the only likely spot for it seemed to be a strip of thin soil at the north end of the station. Then Superintendent Albright became thoughtful. "Let's make a second seeding across the road on better soil."

The result was protein of 11.53 and 16.70 per cent, respectively. Two plot areas, half a mile apart, had produced the lowest and the highest protein of the entire series. Professor Harrison reported:

> Most investigations have gone to prove that there is a greater variation in quality due to climate than to soil. As a matter of fact, there is a greater variation in your two samples than in all the other samples submitted.

> You will be interested to know that the loaf from your good sample was one of the best of all those produced on the Prairie, which again has broken our theory that as you go north on the Canadian Prairie you get a wheat with a smaller amount of protein.

These trials preclude sweeping generalizations concerning a vast region. Bread wheats should have approximately 14 per cent protein. In most years the Peace River production stream ranges from 11 to 16 per cent. Some shipments may test as low as 9.5 per cent, while test varieties at Beaverlodge have soared to 22 per cent protein.

Protein grading is in the offing and could correct some of the ills. Its implementation will create a tremendous administrative problem, one which will call for the utmost consideration of many crucial factors. However, indications are that delivery points will receive protein ratings, thus a wholesale approach. But this approach will place all farms, all farmers, and all conditions in a given locality on a common plane. Certainly this would not be a forward step in encouraging better farming or utilizing agricultural resources fully. At most points a wide range of protein would exist in wheat production and it behooves those concerned to give every advantage to producers who can and do grow wheat of good milling quality.

Following his observations on Ruby wheat, Albright concentrated his attention on Legacy oats. It matured reasonably early, yielded well, and its fine straw made good green feed. The kernel was long and slim so that the samples were not always so attractive as some of the Winnipeg Rust Research Laboratory creations; moreover, it lacked specific disease resistance. Albright, Harris Bros., and others tried resolutely to keep Legacy in the trade but the big market for seed oats was outside the Peace where generally the variety did not find favor. Peace River growers became discouraged with a limited market and so a valuable variety was lost.

However, trainloads of good Victory oats left the Peace year after year during the depression. Crop losses in other parts of Canada focused attention on seed oats from the Peace River region. The Alberta Department of Agriculture used its resources to have the grain cleaned. Portable cleaning equipment was assembled, the prototype of Alberta's fine series of highly efficient farm-operated cleaning plants, and the Peace River Seed Growers Ltd., with Manager W. J. Thompson, handled the marketing. It was a common sight in March to see a score of four-ups from the Halcourt and Elmworth farms wending their way down McNaught's hill with loads of seed oats for markets as far away as Quebec.

Seed inspectors were everywhere. It was affirmed by many that one of them, Aubrey Weir, had a story for every sack to which he affixed His Majesty's Seal. Often it was the way he told the tale; he was always welcome.

On one occasion, Frank Foulds, in charge of the Calgary office, and Aubrey were in the Peace to justify their report that three out of every four of their crop inspectors would be needed there, so great was the interest in seed production. Behind schedule, they arrived at Beaverlodge, battered and torn.

"You see, we were coming over the hill this side of Pouce, Mr. Foulds at the wheel, when we encountered a center-of-the-road driver. Mr. Foulds has traveled a lot but he hasn't knocked around much!"

In 1937 Percy Clubine, then a novice at convention-going, approached Stacey at the Saskatoon convention of the Canadian Seed Growers' Association with the query, "Is there something the matter with me? I don't know these people but they seem to know me!"

"Percy, if you lived in Saskatchewan and had bought Peace River oats for years and if you heard that one of the Peace River growers was here and that he had 13,000 bushels of the finest seed oats in the world, don't you think you'd know who he was?" Stacey asked in return.

The next year Clubine's fame heightened when he produced 134 bushels per acre of registered Victory oats, without fertilizer.

Peace River production was indeed impressive. Victory oats, developed by the Swedish Seed Association at Svalof and introduced into Canadian agriculture in 1911, had had a good run. Jack Welsh of Winnipeg was doing outstanding work in breeding oats but his varieties — Vanguard, Garry, Ajax, and Exeter — were not for the Peace. The Peace River oat varieties are of eastern origin — Macdonald College, Ottawa, and the Maritimes — and the long-time favorite, Victory.

Then there is barley. Not long ago this crop received only casual attention on the part of farmers. It was seeded late or on poorly prepared land. Lodged crops were difficult to bind and more difficult to stook. Smooth-awned and stronger-strawed varieties were developed, while combine harvesting added to the economy and facility of barley production. But still the emphasis was on malting grades, which did aid marketing but encouraged otherwise inferior varieties. Today, production mainly concerns yield.

In 1932, Beaverlodge received from the office of the Federal Trade Commission two packets of barley seed labeled "Grown in southern Finland" and "Grown in northern Finland." Promptly entered as "Finland" and "Lapland," they were subjected to tests. The first seeding of Lapland matured July the twenty-eighth and made a good crop. This was exciting. In type it was ragged, but Stacey would soon see to that.

Three years later, Dr. L. H. Newman, the Dominion cerealist, offered a sack of a new Finnish variety called Olli. "Do you want a sack of seed?"

Stacey did and recognized the purified version of what he had hoped to secure from the Lapland stock. Thus Olli barley came to be licensed. It never received a complimentary word from the trade but for many years it was the backbone of the malting industry and still is, to a considerable extent. It is a reasonably good cropper, sufficiently early to compete with wild oats, can be sown late to extend the seeding season or seeded early and harvested early. Furthermore, it is low in protein, a stringent malting requirement.

Arthur A. Guitard took charge of cereal investigations in 1947. He noted that a few barley varieties had served the Peace well, but the basic needs of the North were yet to be studied. Canada-wide parental stocks had been reworked time and again; foreign countries searched for new blood lines, such as the Olli barley from Finland. The geneticist must really exert himself. As an architect he must outline the needs, then study materials, and move on to methods.

Guitard determined that barley held the greatest potential for the North. He secured co-operation from fellow workers in Alaska, the Yukon, and the Northwest Territories. He found that varieties were highly sensitive to daylight, that they could be classified as long day or short day, and that they were influenced by temperature changes, the so-called Mediterranean stocks used extensively by geneticist Walter Johnston, of Brandon, being unduly sensitive.

It was this change of emphasis which strongly influenced Guitard's research, and in turn his research accelerated barley production in the Peace. In co-operation with Dr. Samuel Litzenberger of the University of Alaska he initiated and co-ordinated the Alcan Cereal tests which for eight years studied performances of several varieties of wheat, oats, and barley at six sites in Alberta, the Yukon, Northwest Territories, and Alaska.

At Beaverlodge, Guitard and his cerealist successor, Dr. Donald Faris, commenced to structure a barley for the North. In theory, find a parent which germinates quickly and establishes itself with dispatch. Then find a parent which has a short development stage to the formation of the head. Then search for a variety which ripens rapidly. The art of crossing is the work of the technician. The parents were readily found in growth-chamber studies and the show was on the road.

The proliferation of hybrid material necessitated a few short cuts and F2 lines were subjected to yield-prediction tests while the chromosomes were being sorted out into variety-making material. Charles Saunders might not have understood the procedures and Stacey was without modern equipment or adequate assistance.

These tests clearly outlined the superiority of barley for production in the North, based essentially on its early maturity, rapid rate of development, and stability under the northern climate. They demonstrated the sensitivity of most varieties of barley to photoperiod, sensitivity to soil nutrient deficiency, and the potential for development through breeding.

This work set the stage for research that was undertaken by Guitard until 1962 when he succeeded Stacey, then retired, as superintendent. It is being continued by Faris, the present cerealist.

It is a long-term program and the search is still on. In theory, Walter Johnston's varieties have limited advantage in the Peace, yet in practice his succession of ever-better varieties for the Prairies has had its impact on the Peace. They may not be perfectly adapted, but in essence they have out-paced the Guitard-Faris stride. "The impossible takes a little longer," and Faris is diligent.

The Noralta flax story is interesting in that a segment of the North, the Lower Peace River region, needed a better variety, one which would mature about as early as the Redwing variety farmers were growing but which would be resistant to rust. Producers knew that Redwing was highly susceptible but because of its early maturity they continued to grow it. Flax acreage was intensified and flax was sown on flax stubble, thus rust developed in epidemic proportions and caused heavy losses in yield.

Some other Canadian varieties were also available but they had been bred for resistance to pasmo and other diseases rampant elsewhere, so were not necessarily better than Redwing for the Fort Vermilion farmers. Another source was several varieties bred in the north-central United States which, though high-yielding, matured much too late for the North.

Dr. Grant McGregor, of Ottawa, visited the Fort Vermilion Experimental Station in the course of duty and as an oil seeds specialist, paid particular attention to the flax trials. None seemed entirely adapted, yet with a truck haul of 200 miles to railhead at Grimshaw and a further 300-mile rail haul to Edmonton, a concentrated, high-value crop such as flax was a must.

This need started a project under technician Jack Newman and later involved A. G. Kusch on his transfer from the Scott Experimental Farm. Hybrids which had been bred and disease-tested at Ottawa were imported and tested. Finally, after a season of adverse growing conditions caused the elimination of most of the lines, the variety Noralta was selected. Tony Kusch had it licensed in 1965.

Thus high-yielding, wilt-resistant Noralta, bred at the Central Experimental Farm at Ottawa, and selected at Fort Vermilion, filled a great need of the North. By happenstance, in a very short time its qualities have made it the most popular Canadian variety.

Kusch was transferred to Beaverlodge in 1965 to continue flax breeding and to investigate rapeseed, now becoming an important crop in the region.

Rapeseed is a new crop for Western Canada and Peace River farmers are beginning to like it. Fortunately the market is expanding and thus rapeseed fills some of the wheat-abandoned acreage. Moreover, it may be seeded late, a valuable asset to those who find their seeding operations extending into June.

The Peace soon found it could grow heavy crops of the early-maturing Polish rape but that the late-maturing Argentine rape was out. Sid Pawlowski, a former Illustration Station supervisor in the Peace and now oil seed specialist at the Research Station, Saskatoon, recognized that the somewhat cold soil of the Peace was an aid to rapeseed production.

Tony Kusch reports Keg River yields of rapeseed were the highest in Western Canada and the quality of oil the best, in a comprehensive test arranged by the Plant Breeders' Committee. Thus Keg River farmers and their neighbors practice a rapeseed-barley-barley rotation, another choice of crops for the Peace.

In a half century there have been many changes; now it seems improbable that the West could have been developed with Red Fife wheat the mainstay, let alone Mead and Grant growing it at Lake Saskatoon. Not only have there been suitable wheat varieties bred for the Prairies but their production has been crowded northward without much thought of the consequences. Now it is obvious that while much of the Prairies is a one-crop region, the North has several crops at its command and barley is better adapted than wheat so long as the emphasis on the latter is for its milling qualities. Someday there will be more emphasis in the less remote North on feed wheat and geneticists have the lines with which to work.

Changing, too, is the concept that the principal cereal crops need be harvested as threshed grain, to be regarded essentially as a cash crop. Late maturing varieties are basically much higher yielding than quick ripening ones while late ripening crops are prey to losses and increased handling costs which readily make them uneconomic. Thus, as the numbers of livestock increase, the Peace will have a valuable new use for a major part of its cereal production — cereal ensilage.

HORTICULTURE

SUPERINTENDENT Albright was greatly concerned that settlers were adequately fed and had favorable home appointments.
For many years his staff mailed out hundreds of packages of strawberry stolons, raspberry roots, currant cuttings, rhubarb roots,
and ornamentals. The recipients were highly grateful. In his
schoolhouse lectures he asked that there be a good garden, a
trim woodpile, and a rocking chair on the veranda.

The settlers did have good gardens. If they concentrated
on the hardy staples — potatoes, rutabagas, carrots, and cabbage — their bins were well filled for winter needs.

But what to grow?

One summer a test was made of thirty-five varieties of
string beans gleaned from seed catalogues, breeding programs,
and the like. It was obvious that only three or four varieties
could be amongst the best. Assistant Superintendent Stacey and
head gardener Wallace each took home samples of the product
daily until all the varieties were eaten. At dinner each night
the samples were duly scored for texture, flavor and color. The
course was served in separate dishes and the families decided
the fate of each variety in turn. All but five varieties proved
highly fibrous. The decision was easy.

On another occasion horticulturist John Moore donned
a chef's hat, cooked up twelve varieties of potatoes and then
invited the administration staff to evaluate. Try it some time:
this variety rates six points for flavor and eight points for
mealiness — or is it the other way around? Neither science nor
amusement; it was a segment of the Peace River story in the
making.

Somehow it all paid off. Potatoes were found to ripen off
better if the seed had formed stubby green sprouts before planting time. Sheet plastic raised soil temperatures and thus con-

tributed to better crops of string beans. Seedling tomatoes fared better in plant bands and even better in six-inch pots. A starter solution added a few days in advance of transplanting, fortified setting-out stocks against handling shock.

Most home gardeners consider the summer incomplete without a few tomatoes ripening on the vine. Under favorable conditions and using seed-trade varieties Peace gardeners could be moderately successful. On one occasion John Wallace had some eighty varieties in his plots, all growing well but only two ripened 'fruit. To the pragmatist, it would be a disaster; to Wallace it was a challenge. The weather records told of a very cool summer and scientific reports stated under such circumstances tomato pollen would not set well in most varieties. Thus began a breeding program which at times involved Wallace, John Moore, Victor Chanasyk, and Dr. Robert E. Harris, bringing together breeding stock from far afield, including selections from Dr. A. Kallio, of College, Alaska.

After many crosses and acres of selection, three outstanding hybrids have been noted, and are being tested at some thirty stations across Canada. They are early ripening with good fruit-setting ability. At some locations the fruit size is faulted.

A second result was that material from the breeding program has been exploited for commercial use and is the basis for the major large-scale production mechanically harvested in the Niagara Peninsula south to the Mississippi Valley.

Another result was the deployment of Winston Charles from the University of West Indies to Beaverlodge, under Canadian International Development assistance, to work with Harris on pollen viability. Just as tomato pollen is adversely sensitive to low temperatures, it is also sensitive to high temperatures, so that in effect, tomato breeding in the West Indies has an affinity to John Wallace's problem at Beaverlodge.

Superintendent Albright was intensely proud of his apple production, noting shortly before his retirement that the crop that year amounted to 1,500 pounds of commercially acceptable fruit. In the initial years it strained his chivalry to give the bow to Mrs. Mary Thompson, on the shores of Bear Lake near Grande Prairie, who had grown seedlings of crab size as early as 1921. At that time he also acknowledged the production of small fruits by Mrs. O. H. Johnson, of Beaverlodge, and John Watson, of Flying Shot Lake.

Albright searched diligently for hardy stocks and several were found amongst the hybrids which Ottawa had developed, using Russian lines. In 1930 Editor George F. Chipman of *Country Guide* sent 1,000 seedlings of mixed breeding. Some very interesting selections resulted and have contributed to the breeding program of the Station. Standard apples and apple-crabs have borne fruit. Several selections are in the final stages of testing, prior to introduction.

Yes, Albright was elated with his apple crops but was brought down momentarily when a commercial orchardist in the Annapolis Valley of Nova Scotia wrote:

> We are in an area of proven apple production, yet are finding difficulty in marketing our crop. It ill behooves you to encourage this production in the Peace and so make it harder for us to survive.

Albright could not agree. He wrote in reply:

> If Canada is to become a great nation, she must develop her resources to the full. There is more to Canada than is found in the confines of the Maritime Provinces. In fact some day that fine region will be but a small segment of the Dominion.
>
> As for apple production, do not fear competition from the Peace for a few years — but it may come eventually, just as the wheat and corn belt is moving north and west.
>
> For the present, consider the delight of a homesteader's family on an isolated bush farm, revelling in the sight of a few apple blossoms in the kitchen garden, or the relish of home-grown crabapple jelly, much superior in flavor to the corner store purchase of an Okanagan Valley product.
>
> Should I tell you of the pride of the Roman Catholic Mission at Fort Resolution on the north shore of Great Slave Lake in its seedling crabapples 10 or 12 feet in height, bearing enough fruit in 1930 to make 720 pounds of good jam?
>
> So let us not be selfish. You should strive to improve your product and a ready market will await your production. For my part I owe a debt of gratitude to the struggling homesteader for the fine efforts he is making.

In 1944 Albright reported:

> When the first apples were planted in 1916, it seemed a forlorn hope that any fruit would ever result but if one

tree bore one or two fruits it would be the means by which experience would be gained through which more trees would bear fruit. Apples, crabapples, plums, pears, cherries, grapes, elderberries and apricots have already been ripened and the 10-acre fruit plantation is looking to the future.

Many fine ornamental crabapples which bloom each spring in home gardens across Canada are of comparatively recent origin. From a group of 300 seedlings of Siberian crabapples received from Dr. W. T. Macoun, Dominion horticulturist, has come Snowcap, pure white bloom on a well-shaped tree. Its acceptance in Canada was slow at first but is gaining momentum. Surprisingly, it is rated highly in the central United States and is reported to be the only ornamental crab resistant to fire blight.

Some Beaverlodge selections of rosybloom crabs have also been outstanding. Arctic Dawn is very attractive, purplish red, from a rootstock of one of the Morden apples. Its use is wide-spread in Western Canada. The late Dr. Frank Skinner, of Drop-more, Manitoba, rated it outstanding for northern areas where hardiness is so important. The variety Albright, with bloom slightly darker than Arctic Dawn, is newly introduced. It is derived from a group of mixed Beaverlodge seedlings.

Apricots fruited but were highly susceptible to late spring frosts. Pears require the mountain of research which has been heaped on the apple across most parts of Canada. Plums and cherries are poorly adapted to heavy soils characteristic of much of the Upper Peace and most varieties carry a high content of tannic acid which discourages domestic use.

Red and black currants are highly successful, as are raspber-ries, with the Trent variety excelling at Beaverlodge.

The Griffin poplar is a hardy, small-leafed variety built like a gas flame. The story goes back to a seedling, a natural hybrid, obtained by Mr. A. Griffin, Superintendent of the C.P.R. Demonstration Farm at Strathmore and an ardent horticulturist, from the banks of the Bow River. Selection No. 4 was named Griffin by the Beaverlodge Station in 1947 and is now widespread in the North. Unfortunately it is not well adapted to the Brown soil region.

The saskatoon bush is native to the region and is highly productive of palatable, edible fruit. What is now the Saskatoon Island Provincial Park was a gathering place for Indians over the years, its acres of berries providing the principal ingredient of pemmican. The long saskatoon hedge planted by Albright in 1916 to flank the driveway of the Beaverlodge Experimental Station was a source of inspiration to visitors for many years.

One afternoon in 1927 Dr. W. T. Macoun, Dominion horticulturist, marked some twenty-seven selections in this hedge, the start of an improvement and breeding program. John Wallace, later head gardener at Beaverlodge, named one of them Smoky, after the nearby Smoky River. Another variety named by Wallace was Pembina, from stock he had sent Albright in 1932 from his trial grounds at Campsie, Alberta. The stock was taken from the wild, in the valley of the Pembina River.

Dr. Robert Harris reports there are approximately eighteen native species of saskatoons in the Peace, but only one is used extensively. Elsewhere it is sometimes known as serviceberry, shadbush, and Juneberry. In 1958 he commenced a breeding program, using material obtained from other parts of Canada, Europe and Asia as well as numerous selections of native stock. Results of the first hybridization were very encouraging, but improvement with one aspect was associated with regression elsewhere. A second round, possibly more, of hybridization will be necessary before decided improvement is obtained.

Fruit analysis and processing tests have been exciting. In a seedling row the fruit may be sweet, rather tart or flat in tests, depending on selection or season. The saskatoon responds well to cultivation and fertilizing. It is suitable for mechanical harvesting and a ready market awaits commercial production. Food processing studies are under way at the University of Alberta but nurserymen have yet to master reproduction difficulties. Public demand for the stock is great and only very limited quantities are available annually.

Routine testing of strawberry varieties continued for years but stocks originated in other parts of the continent and therefore were not truly adapted to Peace River conditions. Winter hardiness was not a problem with the variety Senator Dunlap but the quality was barely acceptable.

Jack Abbott found a likely indigenous selection at Racing River on the Alaska Highway. The Sitka Hybrids of Alaska also offered possibilities but did not transmit acceptable qualities on hybridization. Various wild types of strawberries, including the Racing River strains, were freely crossed and the progeny produced some excellent, though small, fruit and invariably a forest of runners. Porter's Northerner was used in the program but failed to produce size in offspring. Now, Harris has introduced the Protem variety, highly productive of excellent quality fruit and with even greater winter hardiness than Senator Dunlap. Harris is currently giving high priority to breeding for yield and short season of ripening, to develop a variety of strawberry suitable for paid pickers and for mechanical harvesting. He finds many of his hybrids sufficiently hardy to withstand Peace River winters but is searching for even greater hardiness, using electrical conductivity techniques. Harris contends that extensive research into the physiology of winter hardiness is long overdue in the Peace since in most respects the climate is more favorable for overwintering plants than is that of the southern prairie region. Low temperatures in the fall, coupled with bright sunlight and rapidly changing day length, aid plants in their preparation for winter. James McKenzie of the Beaverlodge group is studying these factors so that horticulturists will have a better understanding of plant behavior, which in turn will enhance crop management and breeding programs. It is all very interesting but exceedingly complex.

Superintendent Albright wanted settlers to plant flowers and trees. When the Beaverlodge Experimental Sub-Station was created, Paul Flint, an ex-Methodist minister and member of the 1909 Bull Outfit, was employed as gardener. Mr. Flint was not a scientist but he created a profusion of bloom which brought renewed hope to many a lonely homesteader's family.

By 1928, 287 species of trees, shrubs and ornamentals had been tested by Flint and Albright and the survivors now fill Peace River windbreaks and landscaping ventures. The Manitoba scrub oak grows strongly at the Research Station; the Beaverlodge elm is much better adapted and more stately than commercial stocks of American elm. Oldtimers will recall with pride the west windbreak on the Station grounds.

Speaking of windbreaks, there was serious concern over proper culture. Many homesteaders, including Gordon Sherk, of Huallen, had carefully planted windbreaks according to Indian Head advice — advice which went out to all, regardless of locality. In the Peace some of the trees approaching maturity were not thriving. Close study revealed that the outer rows, which had access to adequate light and moisture, were doing nicely but the inner rows were sickly. Beaverlodge defied tradition and published a bulletin recommending that not more than three rows of deciduous trees be planted in a windbreak.

One of the foremost peony specialists on the continent lived at Teepee Creek. Born of English-West Indian parents, C. M. Clarke was a veteran of World War I. As such, he qualified under the Veterans' Land Act and thereby began a skirmish that knew no end.

Clarke had a good farm and was a good farmer — when he could spare time from his peonies. But VLA Collector Walker must collect accounts.

"What did you do with the proceeds from the grain you sold?"

"Well, five dollars went for food, five dollars for repairs and ten dollars for peony roots."

It was a pleasure to walk down the rows of peonies with Clarke. There were no labels but he knew each variety by sight, by origination, and by International Rating, all 150 varieties. It nearly broke his heart to spend hard-earned money on a much-prized variety for which he had longed eagerly, only to have it turn out to be a Festiva Maxima or a Felix Crousse.

As a member of the American Peony Society Clarke frequently wrote learned articles for its journal. Neighbor W. E. Foore also rated this distinction and was not reticent in presenting his views. In the Society's issue of September, 1943, Foore reported:

> I will give you an idea of contributing conditions which lend themselves to such a wonderful growth in northern Alberta. As you know, this is the country of the Aurora Borealis or Northern Lights which electrify the water. It has been proven that the Northern Lights are an overcharge of electricity. . . . The result is that all the snow is highly electrified.
>
> As I have a natural snow trap and snow falls to a depth of from three to five feet on my peonies and does not melt until late spring, the peonies get the full benefit of the high electrified snow water.

"Tripe," wrote Clarke to the editor.

The C. M. Clarke peony collection is being maintained at the Beaverlodge Research Station and at the University of Alberta.

John Wallace was an ardent horticulturist even as a boy on the family homestead at Campsie, west of Barrhead. After a summer at the Morden Experimental Farm he came to Beaverlodge and served there as head gardener for sixteen years. His first selection was the Nugget Lily. The Beavermor variety of honeysuckle is derived from seed collected by him at Morden in 1943 and has proven very popular on the Prairies. Another Wallace selection, the Wapiti juniper, was introduced in 1952 and has been cited in the *Annals of Horticulture,* Great Britain. The plant is hardy, vigorous, procumbent, and creeping. It grows upright twelve to sixteen inches and has a spread of eight to ten feet. The foliage somewhat resembles that of Savin juniper but in autumn the color turns to dark green with purple overtones which is retained during the winter. It is a selection from the wild state, from the Wapiti River area south of Beaverlodge.

In 1959 John separated to establish a commercial nursery, to provide a better range of suitable planting material for Peace River use and to have freedom to roam the mountains to the west for likely native types with which to further his aims. His service to the region is appreciated and is shared by others across Canada and from as far away as Germany, Holland, and the United States.

The Wallace private introductions are many. Magnared honeysuckle is more winter hardy than the Arnold variety, its competitor on the Prairies. It is developed from seed collected from Percy Wright's Red Giant. Frosty is another honeysuckle, pure glistening white.

From the Two Lakes area in the foothills south of Beaverlodge, Wallace has a six-inch hardy dwarf aster with good prospects for hybridizing. He also has a very ornamental selection of erigeron with one-and-a-half-inch upright lavender flowers in midseason from Thunder Mountain; a Green Island selection of American cranberry bush with excellent fruit; Oregon grape, native at Prince George; and a Racing River lupine with extreme hardiness and all-summer blue bloom.

Possibly the best known introduction by Wallace is the Dunvegan blue juniper, taken from the banks of the Peace River near the Alexander Mackenzie cairn. It is a moderately vigorous grower, prostrate, reaching a height of four to six inches. It forms a springy mass as it matures, with a spread of six to eight feet. The color is steel blue in summer, turning to plum purple in late autumn. It was introduced in 1957 and John received an Award of Merit from the Western Canada Society for Horticulture in 1967. William Cumming, in charge of ornamental horticulture at the Morden Experimental Farm, rates it the outstanding blue juniper on the market and reports that it and the Wapiti juniper are very popular in Western Canada.

Wallace gazes at the Rocky Mountains seen from his nursery and longs for the opportunity to explore their vastness for hardy specimens. The very busy horticulturist occasionally steals off for a day to search in that rugged wilderness scarcely trod by man, yet rich in hardy ornamentals so greatly desired for Canadian landscaping.

Throughout the North there is ample evidence that garden staples can be grown at will, provided a few simple rules are observed. However, like his cousin eastward, a settler can exist on canned goods but in doing so he should not pass indictment on the possibilities of a fuller life. The small group of horticulturists at Beaverlodge, Fort Vermilion, and Fort Simpson, working in co-operation with fellow horticulturists at Edmonton, Lacombe, Brooks, and Lethbridge, have listed some 600 varieties of fruits and vegetables for the North. The list is not complete, but it is impressive considering that only a few professionals and technicians are serving one-third of Canada's land surface.

The North is not given to grumbling; it marches along slowly and steadily. There has been no complaint about the budget for horticultural research. Budgets serve populations and any major Canadian city has a population greater than the entire Peace and its hinterland. Moreover there is scant glamour in potatoes and rutabagas. Horticultural research has served the past well; it will now serve the countless settlers to come.

Perhaps the Albright era has gone. Perhaps now the world is materialistic. The Beaverlodge horticulturists must now plead a commercial cause. Harris was not adverse to this and set out to give a hand to the market gardeners on the benches of the Peace between Dunvegan and Peace River town. The going was not easy at first. Most growers had the spirit but were short on experience. One extensive project had to be delayed for two years until a soiling program restored structure. Even market gardener J. B. Early found that his productive soil suffered from twenty years of continuous cropping. Today, able growers are reaping the fruits of technical aids and improved marketing facilities.

There is a saying in the North that it takes three generations to settle a district and achieve satisfactory production. Whatever generation Gordon Fried, of Flying Shot, is, he has applied himself and taken advantage of every technical aid available to him. He has a good market; his soil is right and water is abundant; he works in close co-operation with professional horticulturist Bob Harris. He has mastered potato production and marketing as well as other lines of vegetables. For several years he has had the most profitable strawberry patch in Canada, operating the largest acreage between central Ontario and the Fraser Valley of British Columbia. His mainstay is the Harris variety Protem.

Much diminished in size but equal in unit production are the current strawberry patches of Tom Nicholson, of Cecil Lake, and ex-Superintendent Stacey. Both use the simple expedient of a generous mantle of planer shavings to reduce moisture loss. Visitors are welcome from early July to late September.

These productions carry a twofold message. One is that it proves that strawberries and other horticultural crops can be grown readily in the Peace, even without the winter protection required in some other regions. Another is the assurance that commercial production is possible to serve the present population and the forthcoming influx.

OUTPOST SERVICE

THE Beaverlodge Experimental Station was built on a philosophy of service to agriculture — particularly the agriculture of the Peace. It offered that service from the first as a small, understaffed unit amid a burgeoning Empire. Albright calculated there were 117,100 square miles in the Peace River watershed and 58,900 square miles in the Athabasca River watershed, compared with about 27,000 square miles in the Clay Belt of northern Ontario. From a nearby promontory, Saskatoon Mountain, he could see at a glance 1,000,000 acres of farm land, more than the entire area of Prince Edward Island. It was untimely to contemplate the extent of the valleys of the Slave, Hay, and Liard rivers and the trunk of the Mackenzie.

In the early years roads in the Peace were almost nonexistent, travel laborious. In step with his schoolhouse talks, Superintendent Albright built up a network of Illustration Stations which served as local points of focus and testing. It was a moot question whether the Station should reach out to where specific problems arose or whether the settlers should be expected to visit the Experimental Station, frequently more than 100 miles distant.

The first unit was set up at Baldonnel, B.C., in the lee of the future Fort St. John airport, on the farm of Jack Abbott, veteran settler with a keen sense of public service.

In 1924 Albright was visited by John Fixter, of Ottawa, in charge of the Illustration Station section of Experimental Farms Service, and the two set out for Baldonnel by team and buckboard, driven by Norman Dow, of Pouce Coupe. Details of the trip are now obscure but one night was spent at the Jimmie Mathews' stopping place near the breaks of the Kiskatinaw River. A pailful of eggs was fed to their host's pigs next morning; eggs at the nearby Kilkerran store were five cents a dozen — if fresh.

The Illustration Station was established and Abbott did painstaking work. His annual field day would equal a Bob Hope-Bing Crosby special, with Officer-in-Charge Abbott insisting on telling his story and Superintendent Albright grabbing at the straws of protocol. On one occasion, Albright was delivering another of his famous lectures in Fort St. John, following a day with the crowd viewing Abbott's plots. At half time, the speaker asked for a recess. Chairman Jack Abbott obliged and after a few well-chosen remarks called for a vote of confidence in the speaker as an invitation for him to resume his talk. The vote was recorded. Many were in favor; others did not bother to register their choice, and the string of teenage girls in the front row were united in their desire to start the dance. The speaker was deflated, the chairman embarrassed. Democracy has its limitations.

Abbott's ambition was to grow alfalfa, queen of all hay crops, and he valiantly grew its seed and sold, traded, or gave it away to neighbors all and sundry. Abbott carried on with his plots and his alfalfa seed production throughout the hectic days of the Alaska Highway construction. Then he was called to investigate agricultural possibilities in the Yukon. His neighbor, H. G. Hadland, one of the outstanding farmers in the entire Peace, was appointed to succeed him.

Bert Hadland's record of public service, good farming, and dedication to production of pure seed is unparalleled. Mr. and Mrs. Hadland now enjoy retirement, living in Fort St. John, summers, and California, winters. When the Canadian Seed Growers' Association held its annual convention in Fort St. John in 1966, Robertson Associate Hadland held the reins and 450 delegates enjoyed true Peace River hospitality. Son Spencer carries on the test plots and the seed growing in traditional Hadland manner.

It is a long jump to High Prairie but there were problems there too. Wild oats could not be controlled by ordinary farming; but on the Illustration Station on the farm of S. J. Fewang, plots of fall wheat and winter rye were free of the weed. Moreover, horsetail grew so vigorously that at times it choked out grain. Intensive study of cultural methods showed that clean plowing in the fallow year would set horsetail back temporarily. Later, Dr. Paul Hoyt of the Beaverlodge Station made a thorough study of control measures by the use of herbicides and all but eradicated the weed, using 2, 4-D on the farm of Sam Jones, of Enilda.

One afternoon after Hoyt's work had been reviewed by Dr. Robert Glen, Director General, Central Experimental Farm, Ottawa, the party retired to the Spaulding, principal hotel and cafe in nearby High Prairie.

"Are you aware, Dr. Glen, that you are now eating where Bruce Hutchison reported in *Maclean's Magazine* that he was served the worst meal on a Canada-wide tour?"

"Don't you believe it," returned Glen. "As a young entomologist I ate in every Chinese restaurant in southern Saskatchewan."

In defense of the august Spaulding, Hutchison had arrived at a time when mud was ankle-deep. Travelers who could reach High Prairie refused to move on and food supplies were almost exhausted.

On a somewhat similar occasion, when Superintendent Stacey had to spend the night in a mudhole on the banks of the Little Smoky River, a fellow traveler refused to complain. Philosophically he settled all arguments at four o'clock in the morning and without supper, observing that "the trouble with us is that we should know enough to travel by saddle horse."

A few years later, High Prairie farmers turned to barley production. Wild oats were under control, yields were excellent, and malting grades were in demand; the rich soil had made growers happy. The Illustration Station test plots were now on the farm of Lawrence Cowell, another master at the game.

At Fairview, Alex McKenzie and, later, Ken McDonald operated another very successful Illustration Station and the entire district responded. Various crop rotations were studied and the causes of the troublesome spring soil erosion were made known. Field days saw a gathering of well-informed farmers wanting to learn, and discussions were lively. Nowadays learning is carried on in the classrooms of the Agricultural and Vocational College across the road.

At Pouce Coupe it was a pleasure to work with Norman Dow. A canny Scot, he had taken some formal instruction in the Maritimes and had served the Soldier Settlement Board for a while. A few years later work was done at Rolla on the farm of the illustrious W. C. Henderson, M.P.

The situation at Progress was different. It was a frontier district and fields were still small. Nevertheless, the annual field day at Henry Bentley's farm was an institution, as it was at Clayton Third's farm at Goodfare. Enthusiasm of the audiences made staff participation a pleasure.

The Gray Wooded soils were not forgotten. Assistance was given at South Wapiti early in the history of that settlement, on the farm of Maurice Lofstrom, and to the Black Duck district north of Fairview on the Illustration Station on the farm of W. H. Smith, and to the Falher-Girouxville district on the farm of A. B. Belanger. At one field day Mr. Belanger proudly pointed to his farm and crop and thanked the Experimental Station for its assistance. "Why, for seventeen years I have made a good living off land some say is not worth owning."

A few miles east of Dreau, major effort was made at McLennan on the farm of Narcisse Lamoureux. This unit, a District Experiment Sub-Station, was selected with great care in co-operation with Soil Survey, as part of a chain to study wooded soils across the northern fringe of settlement from Manitoba westward. The site proved highly suitable for the purpose but its soil still taxed the abilities of a dozen learned agronomists.

Work was commenced in 1946, and two requirements were learned early: Use a grain-sweet clover rotation and work the land carefully at the proper time. In the beginning, it was not possible to send a work crew 165 miles to the dictates of puddling soil; consequently wheat yields were poor—five bushels per acre. Local residents were later wont to wonder at the genius of the Beaverlodge staff as yields increased. The research conducted at McLennan has had far-reaching significance.

One of the most outstanding experiments was a study by Hoyt and Hennig relative to the ability of forage crops to ameliorate the adverse structure of this Gray Wooded soil and thus enhance its productivity. Noteworthy was the build-up from a brome-alfalfa mixture. Not only did the hay crop outyield that produced on the more friable Beaverlodge soil but the succeeding grain crops markedly outpaced those on soil which had been subjected to a grain-fallow rotation, with sweet clover occasionally substituted for bare fallow. The experiment recalled to Stacey the statement of Master Farmer J. L. Paquette, of Donnelly, a few miles away, that the beneficial effect of a red clover seeding was observable seventeen years later. At the time Stacey could scarcely accept the statement without reservation but after the Hoyt-Hennig experiment he felt he owed his friend Paquette an apology.

Most thoroughgoing reports on soil refer to the ARDA classification, a very worth-while index of productivity based on logistics. The verdict is not final, however, as Hoyt and Hennig have raised the potential of the Lamoureux ARDA 4 soil to the Beaverlodge ARDA 7 soil.

In the Battle River district John Nicklason, of Deadwood, an excellent farmer and community leader, ran a splendid Illustration Station for a few years. Plot results served to verify the methods employed throughout the entire farm. Here as elsewhere, service to the public was a matter of professional involvement, tempered by the ability of the operator to cope with local conditions.

Attention was also directed to the Central Peace. Plots on the C. L. Christensen farm at Wanham gave guidance that was sorely needed. Westward at Blueberry Mountain, Jesse James Caterer was another Jack Abbott. He welcomed the Beaverlodge staff and responded to its suggestions; otherwise he carried on in true Western manner — but lawfully. He grew good seed, built an extremely effective grain drier of his own design, and upgraded his neighbors' farming with diplomacy.

"You see, Dr. Glen," he reported, "my weed sprayer is over at the neighbor's. I am finished with it for the season and the neighbor will have his own demonstration which will cause him to buy one for himself next year. I've done this many times before."

This was in contrast to the appeal of Robert McCracken at a meeting near North Star when he begged Ernest Buckingham of the Alberta Department of Agriculture to "tell these people the need for good seed. I've told them and told them but they can't seem to get it through their heads." District Agriculturist George Black and agrologist Stacey exploded, but the populace knew the McCracken approach.

When there was reorganization within the Experimental Farms Service, the Illustration Stations program was discontinued. However, Beaverlodge knew that there were many problems which would be studied to best advantage in the field, whether twenty or 200 miles from the Experimental Station. Consequently it continued its outpost service, even on a greater scale than had been possible heretofore, so that it was not uncommon, when driving down a distant side road, to see a group of staked plots with a sign indicating the significance of the undertaking and thanking the co-operator. The plan was to research the problem, move in to make a comprehensive, intensive study and move on. Everywhere the reception was excellent; most farmers shared the spirit of Les and Rowe Harris: "The Beaverlodge Station can put plots on our land at any time and we shall be grateful."

We are reminded that education is a provincial prerogative and agricultural extension is education. When W. D. Albright toured the country schools and district halls, he had research to report but his major contributuion was to teach, and to encourage settlers to become sound and satisfied citizens. Today, Canada offers the Canadian Broadcasting Corporation. But in Albright's time he had little company. There was a District Agriculturist, then another; a District Home Economist, then another; the Soldier Settlement Service Board supervisor . . . and more recently, representatives of industry and trade.

As others moved in, the Experimental Station could get on with its own tasks, though it must always reserve the right, initially, to report its findings through whatever channel it deems best. Furthermore, its research officers must be sheltered from the casually curious.

Another consideration bears comment. All competent researchers and extensionists are professionals. Advice can be based on fact, or on opinion tempered with experience. It is expedient that such advice be sorted carefully, else the producer may be victimized.

In 1935 Albright saw the problems; service to farmers— some of whom were new to the country—must expand. Distances were too great for the ready exchange of thought. He called a conference to co-ordinate professional thinking and added a few leading farmers for ballast. It met with excellent response and co-operation. The conference became an annual affair and attracted attention throughout the province. A few skeptics were unable to understand how federal and provincial workers could sit with mutual tolerance at the same table. There was no time for personalities—get on with the job!

This arrangement went well, but again, it was a case of the Beaverlodge Experimental Sub-Station filling a vacuum. Surely it was, instead, the responsibility of others.

A break came in 1958 with the formation of the Peace River Branch of the Alberta Agricultural Institute. Once more the Peace had to be different. Federal and provincial bylaws were searched and stretched to recognize the wishes of the Alberta and British Columbia agrologists to work together. Finally, when the AIA-BCIA was well established, it was handed the answer on a platter—a co-ordinating conference. It continues to serve well, with minor amendments, although the Albright shadow rests lightly on the shoulders of a new generation.

Another attempt was made to serve agriculture. Superintendent George DeLong of the Lacombe Experimental Station, listening to leaders of farm groups, became aware that an information gap existed. To bridge the void, Experimental Stations at Lethbridge, Lacombe, and Beaverlodge, in conjunction with the United Farmers of Alberta, instituted liaison conferences in their respective regions. The U.F.A. nominated representatives of its component groups such as poultry producers, cattlemen, and grain growers, who sat down with members of professional research staffs to state their relative responsibilities and outline problems. Thus producer representatives could report more accurately the meaning of research, and the research staffs could learn, firsthand, problems of the producer.

The meetings were informative and provocative. Initially, the Beaverlodge research staff sensed that they were on trial, but Superintendent Stacey reminded them that those with findings to report owed producers this service. Some producers were in awe of the scientists but came to know these public servants as agreeably human; some producers represented their groups objectively; others in terms of self-interest.

The Liaison Committee continues to meet the Beaverlodge staff and the arrangement has been effective. Les Harris, a veteran member, is a strong proponent of the cause of the producer.

THE DEVELOPING NORTH

IN THE DAYS of the fur trade, Fort Vermilion was an important, strategic point. At one time it had a greater population than Winnipeg. In 1907, it consisted of about 500 people, white and English-speaking half-breeds.

Dr. G. M. Dawson, assistant director of the Geological Survey of Canada, reported on his trip into the Peace River country before a Senate Committee in 1907:

> Fred Lawrence, F.R.G.S., Justice of the Peace, etc., of Fort Vermilion, gave some detailed and interesting evidence . . . Mr. Lawrence explained that his father, E. J. Lawrence, went out into Peace River from Montreal in 1879 in the employ of the Church of England missions, becoming at once interested in the problem of making the missions and Indian schools in Peace River and the whole of the northern country, self-sustaining.
>
> The total production of wheat there in 1906 would be 25,000 bushels, the average being about 21 bushels to the acre. The wheat was ground and used to make bread for the people there. The first market was at Fort Vermilion and surrounding points, and whatever surplus there was was shipped down the Peace River to the Mackenzie River district.

Fred Lawrence, who later operated a flour mill at Lake Saskatoon about the time of Albright's arrival in the Peace, was the first to conduct tests there. On creation of the Sub-Station Experimental Farm at Fort Vermilion in 1908 Lawrence was succeeded by Robert L. Jones, believed to be Stoney Point district's first homesteader (1892), and whose legendary record would have crowded Tug Boat Annie from the pages of the *Saturday Evening Post*.

For years the settlement depended on riverboat transportation. The Mackenzie Highway was pushed through during World War II to expedite shipments of uranium ore from Eldorado to power the bombs which fell on Hiroshima. Finally, the Great Slave Lake Railway was built in 1964 to transport the lead-zinc ore from Pine Point. The town of Fort Vermilion was now only forty-five miles from rail service.

Descendants of fur-trade days have remained. Mennonite groups, seeking isolation, found refuge and became good farmers. In the depression years of the 1930's a group of Ukrainians from east of Edmonton centered on Peace River town and built rafts, powered by their tractors. The flotilla was dubbed "The Russian navy" as it carried its passengers to new homes east of High Level.

Frank Jackson landed at Carcajou, cut a wagon trail ten miles or so to Keg River, and was assessed stumpage for his efforts. Keg River settlement is located on some of the best soil north of Edmonton. At Keg River and Fort Vermilion it is not unusual to find cob corn in gardens and top grades of grain.

It must have been discouraging to early settlers to sack their grain and line it up on the shores of the Peace River at Tompkins Landing for transport by riverboat to market at Peace River Landing, or to learn the Hudson's Bay Company flour mill or the Sheridan Lawrence mill could not use all of it. It must have been cumbersome to crowd hogs and cattle onto the boats. Nevertheless the settlement in the Lower Peace held on. Now, producers market their crops readily, though still at heavy expense, at points along the Great Slave Lake Railroad and at Grimshaw and Yellowknife.

The settlers have never expected instant prosperity and have rarely found it. The easiest money has come from flax and alfalfa seed, and, lately, rapeseed. Alex Charnetski, Livestock Promoter for the Alberta government, despaired that their cattle showed poor breeding. Improvement is now under way.

Yes, development has been progressing but not always at the rate rumored. On one occasion, visitors contributed their share to the news of the day.

William Dickson, editorial assistant to Director Archibald, was periodically called on to report meetings or to write speeches. One morning, before breakfast, he stood on the banks of the Peace at Fort Vermilion and talked with an oldtimer. Minutes later, while breakfasting at Lambert's Hotel, he suggested that those who would come to Fort Vermilion in ten year's time would travel by rail. His authority — the man at the river.

An hour later Dickson reported for work at the Fort Vermilion Experimental Station and was welcomed with news that in ten years time a railroad would be built to the Fort. The authority — a visitor from Ottawa, staying at Lambert's Hotel.

Is not moccasin telegraph the stock-in-trade of newspaper reporters?

Robert Jones was followed by Bert Lawrence, as Officer-in-Charge of the Sub-Station. Lawrence in turn was followed by Victor Lowe. Both served the district well and encouraged isolated settlers to follow the newer trends of agriculture which were being developed in more settled regions.

Henry Anderson was transferred from Beaverlodge in 1956 to become the first scientifically-trained superintendent of the Fort Vermilion Experimental Farm. Hank continued the crop production studies which had been successful in his former post and as a result of this and improved transportation, agriculture commenced to move forward. A. G. Kusch was moved in from the Scott Experimental Farm to assist Anderson and to head cereal investigations, which to this time had been handled so ably by plotman Jack Newman. In 1963 Anderson was moved on to head the soil fertility section of the Swift Current Experimental Farm and in 1965 Tony Kusch was transferred to Beaverlodge. That year Ben Siemens was appointed Superintendent.

Fort Vermilion has long been an important link in the research chain. It has been a member of most uniform testing programs whereby new cereal and fertilizer practices are investigated. Like Beaverlodge, it has extended its influence into distant points such as Keg River and Buffalo Head Prairie, even unto Hay River and Fort Smith. Anderson and Siemens have followed Soil Survey into Savage Prairie, where there is a considerable tract of acid soil.

The isolation of the region is being dissipated by improved transportation services. Nevertheless crops are produced at a considerable distance from major markets. Potentially, however, the Lower Peace exceeds that of the present development of the entire Peace.

Farther north, Ottawa had established a few sub-stations at the Missions along the Mackenzie. Packets of seeds were sent out each spring. Reports were encouraging and enthusiastic — at Providence the carrots were "lovely" and at McPherson the potato crop was "amazing" — but scarcely scientific. Such evaluations would stop even today's sophisticated computers. Also, there had been one or two sorties of research personnel into the region on a hit-and-run basis. These amounted to someone hopping off a riverboat, asking a hundred questions and catching the boat again, leaving the bewildered local citizens mystified.

Much to Albright's delight, he was commissioned to travel down the Mackenzie River in 1930 to assess agricultural possibilities. The Superintendent went north, somewhat sharing the popular misconception that it was an unproductive land, unfriendly to garden lovers. But he found himself very much at home chatting with William and Christina Gordon in their flourishing garden at Fort McMurray and with their neighbor, Cecil Potts, discussing horticulture. He completely regained his optimism when John Goodal at Fort Simpson reported a 25-to-1 increase in Netted Gem potatoes and Father Robin at the Mission told of the rapid growth of tomatoes.

At Albright's suggestion, the priest documented his statement with tomato vines measuring 10¾ inches on July the seventh; 21½ inches on July the fourteenth, and 24 inches on July the seventeenth. At Fort Norman Father Haussais had potatoes 6 inches high on July the fifteenth and an inch higher each day for the following week. Albright could scarcely believe such changes were possible.

Oscar Granath, a Swede living seventy miles below Fort Norman, reported using potatoes fifty-five days from planting.

William Clark, of Thunder River, eighty miles north of the Arctic Circle and 965 miles north of Edmonton, told Albright of throwing lettuce away by the armsful into the nearby bush where, under a thin layer of muskeg, the permafrost was from six to twelve inches of the surface. Clark was an excellent gardener by any standards. That year of 1930 his potatoes averaged 370 bushels per acre from non-sprouted sets. His fifty cabbages weighed eight pounds or better, with other staple vegetables in good supply. In 1931 he reported a less favorable season, with frost on July the twenty-sixth which affected his beans and potatoes. However, the first frost in 1932 was not until

September the fifth and that year Clark ripened one or two pumpkins.

Albright also visited trapper Knud Lang at Aklavik, 1,015 miles north of Edmonton, and saw barley samples from the Beaverlodge Station seed ripening a few inches above permafrost. Gardens were flourishing and he saw rhubarb with stalks large enough to use for pies. In the bush along the River, spruce grew eight to ten inches in diameter. Here he found permafrost was six to eight inches below the surface, as reported by Alexander Mackenzie 141 years earlier.

By the time Albright reached Herschel Island, he had run out of gardens but cheerfully reported "wild flowers grew in mass effects of the richest hues."

Seventeen years later Stacey was authorized by Director Archibald to make a similar tour of the region annually, with stops at Fort Vermilion, Mile 1019 on the Alaska Highway, Fort Simpson, and Yellowknife. The purpose of the visitation was to maintain liaison, make comparative studies of results, and to serve as guide to various divisional officers who could find time to spend the heart of the summer learning about one-third of the Canadian expanse and who wanted to be associated with its development.

This tour was continued for six years, after which Frank Nowosad, of Ottawa, was appointed to co-ordinate agriculture in Canada's North, from Fort Chimo in northern Quebec to the Yukon, on a full-time basis.

Fort Simpson is a settlement as old as the fur trade, a strategic point on the Mackenzie River. It was still a trading center when the first Stacey tour was made in 1948 despite the influence of the Canol Project and an adequate airport. The year before, the paddle wheeler *Distributor* was in its last season on the river.

John Gilbey had arrived in 1947 to set up an Experimental Farm to serve the Mackenzie region, with supplies delivered by water. The supplies were unloaded box by box, but somehow a pile of his chimney bricks slipped overboard. The bricks were salvaged by Indian youths, digging their toes into the river sand as the water line receded, and were retrieved at five cents a brick, F.O.B. Gilbey's office. In due time the superintendent's house was built by the most skilled Indian labor available.

"Do you see? Cut this board this long and nail it here," Gilbey directed patiently. Half an hour later, returning to the construction site, he would repeat, "See this board? Cut it this long and nail it here." Eventually the house was built but it did tax Gilbey's patience at times. Other government agencies had their construction crews flown in from Edmonton, at union rates and overtime, to erect staff quarters. No one could explain the double standard, save that agrologists are basically farmers and farmers are provident.

The Bert Neelin boat was usually the first to arrive in the spring, down the Liard River from Fort Nelson. Once the cargo was to include a dozen freshly killed chickens for Superintendent Gilbey, a tasty morsel after eating canned ham all winter.

"Sorry, John," Neelin apologized, "I made a mistake and unloaded your chickens at Fort Liard. But I'll tell you what I'll do. I've fifteen chickens for Aklavik and they'll never miss 'em." It was the way of riverboat captains.

At that time, Indians at Fort Simpson were a dejected lot. They would stand at the agency's medical center for hours waiting the convenience of the doctor for a pill; bide their time patiently at the agency for a chit to buy a few groceries. Hungry and dejected they would slink off the road at the approach of a white man.

Soon Gilbey had no difficulty growing an excellent garden and entered his products at the local fall fair in competition with the Catholic Mission and the Hudson's Bay Company. Many Indians developed successful gardens as well, but lacked winter storage facilities, so that their diet was limited much of the year. Gradually their position improved; the Indian population are now eating better and are walking proudly.

Fort Simpson now has modern schools. Mrs. Dick Turner's restaurant with its choice of canned meat balls or meat balls and spaghetti is probably replaced by a drive-in, and Andy Whittington's stopping place by a hotel. The settlement will soon be served by a bus line. A highway is projected to Fort Liard, sixty miles westward, to meet the P.G.E. railroad extension from Fort St. John.

But Gilbey was not altogether happy. For one thing, there was the Albert Faille shack in the middle of his experimental grounds. Now, Albert was a good neighbor and spent his sum-

A smooth field of Black soil in the Halcourt district cut in two by a six-foot gully, the result of severe erosion, 1935. — W. D. Albright photo

Honey in the making; an out-apiary in the Hinton Trail district, serving to pollinate a field of alsike clover, 1964.— Canada Agriculture photo

Alfalfa field on the farm of Baline Pierce, Clayhurst, B.C., 1939. For several years this field produced about 400 pounds of choice seed annually. — W. D. Albright photo

Sweet corn fodder shocked for livestock feed on the J. B. Early Market Garden, south of Berwyn, Alberta, 1931. Shown are J. B. Early and W. D. Albright. — W. D. Albright photo

Gordon S. Moyer stooking his 110-bushel-per-acre oat crop in the Elmworth district, 1928.
— McDermid Studio photo

Picking saskatoon fruit in a selection row, Beaverlodge Experimental Station, 1964. —
Canada Agriculture photo

Seedling tomatoes from a breeding program at the Beaverlodge Research Station which resulted in the introduction of a dwarf "Sub-Arctic" type which is now revolutionizing commercial production in many parts of the world. — R. E. Harris photo

Some 83 varieties or strains of apples or ,rabapples bore fruit at the Beaverlodge Experimental Station, 1944. — W. D. Albright photo

Field peas, Beaverlodge Experimental Station, July 12, 1926. The Chancellor variety, right, yielded 56 bushels per acre. — W. D. Albright photo

Testing flax varieties, Beaverlodge Experimental Station, 1936. — W. D. Albright photo

Harvesting oat plots, Beaverlodge Experimental Station, 1926. The yields were 134-146 bushels per acre. — W. D. Albright photo

Haying test plots of alfalfa, Beaverlodge Experimental Station, 1935. This first cutting yielded 2.5 tons per acre. Standing, L-R: John Cussack, Cornelius Fast, and Lawrence Oszust. — E. C. Stacey photo

Harris Bros., of Beaverlodge, picking up a swathed creeping red fescue seed crop.

Bulk handling of creeping red fescue seed. — Canada Agriculture photo

Machine-run creeping red fescue seed in storage awaiting processing. Much of it is purchased in one-pound lots in the supermarket to seed newly-prepared lawns. — C. R. Elliott photo

Sacked creeping red fescue being loaded on a tandem truck for transport to a central cleaning plant. — Canada Agriculture photo

Creeping red fescue aftermath in late summer, awaiting late fall or winter pasturing. —
C. R. Elliott photo

Midwinter pasturing on creeping red fescue. — C. R. Elliott photo

William D. Clark in his vegetable garden at Thunder River, N.W.T. on the Mackenzie River, 80 miles north of the Arctic Circle, 1938. — E. Clark photo

Rev. Father Adam, O.M.I. in his garden at Inuvik, N.W.T. — Canada Agriculture photo

Jock Aitchison picking raspberries, Fort Vermilion Experimental Station. — Canada Agriculture photo

Dennis Collison's Toad River Ranch, Mile 422, Alaska Highway, 1964. — Canada Agriculture photo

The Experimental Station at Mile 1019, Alaska Highway, showing pipes for sprinkler irrigation to prevent frost damage to crops. — Canada Agriculture photo

Beef cattle at the Experimental Station, Mile 1019, Alaska Highway, after wintering in an open-faced shelter. — Canada Agriculture photo

mers searching for gold up the Nahanni where his name is still legend. He was also a hold-over from the old regime, which scarcely recognized the need for an experimental farm. Gilbey must bide his time.

Gilbey's other problem lived in the swamp over by the snye — some twenty nesting sandhill cranes. Protected by the Canadian Wildlife Service from extinction, these enormous birds, taking the air with their grating call, would land on Gilbey's plots. The R.C.M.P. were sympathetic but there was a law. To Gilbey, the mating call of the sandhill crane was even less musical than the caw of the Yellowknife raven.

Gilbey's official visitors could not comprehend, scientifically, the phenomenon of moccasin telegraphy. One evening while seated on the banks of the Mackenzie River at Fort Simpson they saw a canoe drifting downstream, a mile away. The Indian boys, also watching, shouted, "Billy Beaverskin is on his way to Wrigley!"

How did they know? Simple. It was a family of four who last week went up to Providence and before long were to visit relatives at Wrigley. Who else could it be?

John Gilbey did a remarkable job of representing agriculture amid a setting of Northern Affairs and Wild Life. All summer he would hop along the Mackenzie from Fort Smith to Aklavik, with one student at Fort Simpson and another at Yellowknife. He represented his department but his primary concern was the training of Indians to become more self-provident.

Travel was difficult. On one occasion Stacey and Gilbey were at Yellowknife, about to return to Fort Simpson. The charter with Associated Airways had been laid on, so all was well. But along came the mining recorder, bound for Radium. The book showed that the charter was assigned to him. This was no major crisis in bush country. The parties pooled their resources; the plane would fly the mining official to Radium then the rest to Simpson via Norman Wells, at Gilbey's insistence.

Everything went according to plan until midday. The plane was over Gun Barrel Inlet, a few miles out of Radium, with no lunch on board.

"Simple. We'll drop down to Gun Barrel Inlet and eat fish."

The party set down and Stacey was handed a rod and told

to cast. Amateur fisherman at best, he was astounded to take three large lake trout in five casts. By then the camp fire was blazing.

But pilot John David was unhappy. "Last week I was at Lake Saskatoon flying gasoline to Monkman Lake and left my briefcase on the dock." Stacey saw John a week later in Edmonton and learned that Justyn Rigby, custodian of Saskatoon Island Provincial Park near Beaverlodge, had seen to it that the briefcase was returned to its owner. Today Gun Barrel Inlet is the setting for a fishing lodge at rates starting at about one hundred dollars a day.

At Normal Wells the Imperial Oil Ltd. guest house featured a mammoth frigidaire in the common room but no other furniture. At least refreshments could be served, chilled. Food in the large mess hall was excellent. The cook was jubilant, explaining that only that afternoon he had intercepted a shipment of thirty bags of potatoes at Lower Hay some 500 miles away which would arrive the next Thursday. This was fortunate because the present supply would run out by Wednesday. The supply depot normally was at Edmonton, 1,000 miles distant. There are no supermarkets at Norman Wells.

At the airport a dozen cargo planes were lined up, waiting take-off clearance for the Dew Line.

Benefiting from his wartime experience at Ste. Clothilde and at Goose Bay airport, John Gilbey maintained good plots on the patch of muck soil at Yellowknife. Dennis Callaghan, the proprietor, was his problem. His truck farm was good — and bad. If it was good, Dennis, in true Irish fashion, would have cause for celebration; if ailing, he would listen intently to Gilbey and to all others. Garrulous and colorful, Dennis told Dr. Goulden of a friend who "has nothing upstairs but a hat rack" upon which the worthy scientist, a bit taken aback by the allegory, maybe wondered if the tale had local application.

It was encouraging to drive through the residential area of Yellowknife and note gardens flourishing on sheer pre-Cambrian rock and a load of peat moss. It had been intriguing to see Yellowknife develop, with all the problems associated with the creating of a new townsite. On Stacey's first visit the trenches for water lines had been opened up to melt the permafrost. Vic Ingram's hotel was awesome, and three of the four automobiles belonged to a taxi firm which boasted "intercom" service; even so, two of its vehicles collided shortly afterwards and this allowed the dust to settle. On a later visit the banquet speaker proclaimed the coming 1970 Centennial of the Northwest Territories. He talked about the Arctic Games which would attract skiers from Norway and Sweden. It would be a mammoth gala and the Territories would come into their own.

"And we shall send a strong delegation to Ottawa demanding the return of certain lands which have been alienated from the Territories — namely Manitoba, Saskatchewan, and Alberta. We don't want British Columbia!"

In a very short time Gilbey could be well satisfied with his program. He had instituted crop rotations to study fertility, conducted uniform tests of cereals to determine variety suitability to the region and their comparative reaction to climatic factors.

His garden at Fort Simpson rivaled Edmonton gardens in perfection and production. The gardens of Jack Browning, of Trout River, and William Clark, of Arctic Red River, supplied winter vegetables to settlements down the river to Aklavik. In 1956 the Beaverlodge Experimental station established a testing station at Inuvik and Dr. Harris of Beaverlodge reported the successful production of a large number of vegetables and flowers, using fertilizer, plastics, and other techniques. Even such crops as strawberries, rhubarb, and perennial onions did well.

Westward from Fort Simpson lies the valley of the Liard River. When Rev. A. C. Garrioch visited Fort Simpson in the late nineteenth century he heard William Findlay expound on the climate and soil of the Upper Liard. Many years later Albright also heard tales of good soil, good climate, big trees, and songbirds in the valley. Trapper Alvin LeFlair wrote that he would sow his garden in the spring and at freeze-up return for the harvest, with scarcely a failure. Rev. Fr. J. C. Lefèbre told Albright of very successful farming and gardening efforts at Fort Liard and believed the whole region of the Liard to be as favorable for cultivation as the Peace. John A. McDougal, one-time chief government official in the Mackenzie District shared this opinion.

Should the reader be skeptical about these areas when Premier W. A. C. Bennett committed his government to extend the P. G. E. Railroad to the Liard? No doubt there are scores of unpublished reports to support this expenditure of public funds.

South of the Liard Valley lies the Fort Nelson Plateau, which in turn sweeps further south, almost as far as Keg River. The principal settlement, at Fort Nelson, was important to the fur trade. Then came an airport, followed by the discovery of huge reserves of natural gas and oil in the vicinity. The population of Fort Nelson is about 3,500 persons, with an equal number of transients following the gas strikes.

Stacey first heard of the Nelson Plateau from Frank Jackson, of Keg River, who spoke glowingly of its extent and of its possibilities for ranging cattle. More recently Arnold Hennig of Beaverlodge has grown crops in the Fort Nelson region and claims it is one of the few remaining frontiers of considerable potential, both industrial and agricultural. The land elevation lies between 1,000 and 1,500 feet above sea level, compared with 2,200 to 2,500 feet near Grande Prairie. The climate compares favorably with that at Beaverlodge and appears suitable for a wide variety of field and garden crops. Much of the land is heavily treed, hence lumbering and pulp mill operations may precede large-scale farming and, together with the oil industry, will open roads. Cattlemen tell of bunch grass and light snowfall west of Fort Nelson and seem ready to move in.

Perhaps the reader will recall the Northwest Staging Route, established in 1920 by General Billy Mitchell, who sent four DeHavilands, under the command of Captain St. Clair Streett, to Edmonton, Prince George, Wrangell, Whitehorse, Dawson, and Fairbanks. By 1922 bush pilots were flying this country and into isolated areas.

With World War II came realization that Alaska was no more distant from Russia than England was from the Continent; that food reserves in Alaska would carry the population for only one month and that in the event of invasion from Japan, military forces would not want to cope with domestic difficulties. A highway must be built from the settled area of northwestern Canada. But what route? Four plans were considered. One had the highway reaching north from Dawson Creek, the inland route. Thus there was subdued excitement in the Pullman car which left Edmonton for Dawson Creek on the afternoon of

January the thirtieth, 1942. The stateroom was occupied, a rare happening; the occupants had a steady stream of the visitors. Soon it was learned that the excitement centered on General William M. Hogg, Corps of Engineers, U.S. Army, who was to make a last-minute reconnaissance of the Northwest Staging Route, later to be known as the Alaska Highway. A few days earlier, Canada's Vilhjalmur Stefansson of Arctic Exploration fame, had recommended the route as it avoided the heavy snows of alternate routes to the west.

The Peace sprang to life. On March the ninth, 1942, Dawson Creek had a population of 400; on March the tenth the village exploded to a population of 4,000. A contingent of the United States Army had arrived to build the highway. The leisurely, twice-weekly Northern Alberta Railway passenger service was increased to daily service, some trains running in two sections and freight trains twenty minutes apart. The dirt highway took the remaining traffic, and a beating. At Dawson Creek, because of restricted river ferry service across the Peace, north-bound trucks left at two-and-a-half minute intervals day and night. A three-ton military truck took two-and-a-half-ton loads, a commercial truck seven tons. It was a harvest for all who could leave their farms and the pay was good.

The Alaska Highway was well constructed and graveled, all in the record time of slightly more than six months, to punch 1,756 miles through wooded and sometimes mountainous country.

Northern Canada and Alaska were eye openers to the young soldiers and the construction workers from the United States. Black troops watched vigilantly for crocodiles in the Peace and refused to believe men could walk across the river in winter. Many wanted to return after the war, to open a hot-dog stand or to file on land. What were the prospects for agriculture north of Fort St. John?

Dr. Alfred Leahey, soil specialist from Ottawa, spent the summers of 1943 and 1944 on the Alaska Highway and reported that a headquarters should be set up at Mile 1019 near the base camp at Mile 1016, to conduct farming operations and generally to guide possible settlement in those parts. Jack Abbott, of Baldonnel, B.C., was the man to take charge, He arrived on October the fourth, 1944, and promptly responded with the enthusiasm of the pioneer. He found the going hard but results were satisfactory. His garden might be favored by only one good rain in the summer, nevertheless it produced well.

Abbott cultivated the attention of anyone who would talk farming or ranching. Most settlers were weekend ranchers with more optimism than experience and almost all were moonlighting from highway jobs. Development came and went, lasting until the treasury became depleted. A new crop of incumbents was always in the making and everyone wished them well. One entrepreneur, departing from the prevailing crop pattern, established a fine herd of cattle and on slaughtering most of them, brought the meat to the kitchen of a nearby mine. It was rejected; the contract with the Miners' Union called for inspected meat; the nearest inspector was in Vancouver.

Abbott fared better with a group of bona fide farmers from the Lacombe district who ventured north in 1953 and bought a ranch on the Pelly River. The partners, Hugh and Dick Bradley, John Stelfox and Buck Godwin, worked in earnest and broke up 200 acres of sod-bound hayland, bought a few head of cattle, hogs, and some poultry.

In 1967 they harvested 48 tons of excellent potatoes from six acres. Their barley averaged 45 bushels, oats 55 bushels, and wheat 30 bushels per acre.

The Bradley brothers remained on the farm and in 1969 reported a disastrous summer from forest fires and summer frost.

Such is the experience of the settlers, ready to cast their lot and accept a few hardships. Disturbing, though, in that isolated region is their concern regarding water pollution from up-stream mining operations which may kill the salmon, grayling, inconnu, and other fish and may eventually render the water unfit for human use. It is difficult to develop the agricultural potential of a region when industry can obliterate many of its resources if unchecked.

Originally the Bradley land was secured as three homestead leases in 1903, to provide grain, beef, hogs, and garden produce to Dawson City. A hammermill, known as the first flour mill of the Yukon, ground flour from the wheat. Paddlewheelers, running the Yukon from Whitehorse to Dawson City, periodically ran the five miles up the Pelly to take on farm products.

The homesteads became amalgamated into a ranch which was bought by Frank Fairclough, a lumberman. About 1924 he sold the land to Chapman and Olsen, who went into cattle in a big way. They, in turn, sold to J. C. Wilkinson, about 1940, who continued to raise stock and did considerable trapping and freighting.

In 1907 the Royal North West Mounted Police reported a farm of ninety acres five miles from the mouth of the Pelly, producing hay and oats. The oats ripened and were put through the first threshing machine in the Yukon Territory, with an estimated yield of thirty-five to forty bushels per acre.

The Klondike Dairies, a few miles up the Yukon River from Dawson City, was established during the gold rush (1897-1899) and flourished. The Ackland farm on the Yukon near Dawson grew a wide range of field crops and vegetables.

From 1915 to 1925 an Experimental Sub-Station was operated by James R. Farr at Swede Creek on the left bank of the Yukon River about six miles from Dawson, where a good range of crops, particularly brome grass, was produced.

Abbott's location was some 1,080 miles from Beaverlodge — further than from Beaverlodge to Winnipeg. Stores in Whitehorse were busy. When the impatient Abbot went into the Taylor & Drury Department Store with what he thought was a huge order, the management smiled, passed the time of day briefly, and suggested that the customer might wish to return the next day to list his requirements with one of the clerks.

Then too, there was the game of confusing the Highway Authority. Was the pile of lumber on the side of the road at Cracker Creek yours for the taking? Or if taken, would it land you in jail? The game was played all ways, day and night. War Assets would have office desks in Building 25; the holder of a warrant to choose one would soon learn to make his selection early, to take the best, and, if convenient, to take the mahogany one from the front office and to move fast.

Abbott found farm help amongst the Indians, as did John Gilbey at Fort Simpson. They might set their own periods of work but they could repair any mechanical device with dispatch. The importation of poultry caused much excitement. To his most faithful native worker, Abbott explained, "See, you feed it but you don't eat it."

When test plots of cereals at Mendenhall Flats were being marauded by Columbia ground squirrels — gophers to prairie folk — Abbott set out poison. The Indian women reported him to the Indian Agent for eroding their food supply and an official letter was sent to Superintendent Abbott to desist.

A string of airports was built along the Alaska Highway — Grande Prairie, Fort St. John, Fort Nelson, Watson Lake, and Whitehorse — at 300-mile intervals and with emergency landing strips between each. Beyond Fort St. John, these airports and emergency landing strips were selected mostly on sandy locations and thus cross winds could carry grit which would cut out the airplane motors. The situation was serious, particularly at Whitehorse. Engineers had their plans — acres and acres of hard surface at tremendous expense. However, George DeLong, Superintendent of the Lacombe Experimental Farm, hearing of the problem, became a one-man committee to stop such nonsense. A farm-trained operator, a few bags of seed, and a ton of fertilizer would do the job.

With the plan in operation, Superintendent Stacey accompanied DeLong on a tour of inspection. The visiting party consisted of the pilot to deliver mail and groceries; two agronomists of note; an inspector from War Assets checking on a missing pile of bricks, seven lengths of pipe, and other unaccounted-for items; and a mechanic who was always asleep before the plane lifted and always awake when it touched down. Some doubted that he was helpful to War Assets, that through him the grapevine told the tale of bricks and pipe before investigation could be commenced with due formality, hence neither bricks nor pipe was found.

It was a memorable trip. The service aircraft left Fort St. John at noon; there was no stewardess on board and no lunch. The seat was a convenient nail keg in the rear of the cabin. The inspection party, welcomed at each of a dozen airports or emergency strips with perfunctory courtesy, made its observations as best it could and was on its way. It was noted that seedings had been highly successful but would require frequent fertilizing.

On approaching Snag field it was recalled that the previous winter, temperatures had dropped to 81 degrees below zero and words froze in the air! When the party arrived, the temperature was 81 degrees above. The work crew, busy shuffling painted rocks which marked the pathway to the Officers' Quarters, to demonstrate troop morale to the visitors, were almost exhausted from heat exposure.

It was a pleasure for Jack Abbott at Mile 1019 to show his visitors the salmon drying racks of the Klukshu Indians. Lunch at the divide a few miles farther down the Haines Highway, with the St. Elias Mountains to the north, was miserably chilly; a misty breeze sent even the coffee pot into a deep freeze. Dr. Cyril Goulden, world-famed cerealist and statistician, roaming the valley below, found an abandoned oil barrel with a quart of contents remaining, a prize he trundled end over end back to camp. Wearing his peanut-straw hat, Dr. Goulden needed little make-up to resemble a peon and apart from the temperature, the setting could have been Mexico. He was quickly learning the scrounging techniques of the Alaska Highway.

It was "unbelievable" to pomologist Don Blair to see a tomato ripening on the vine when the weather office reported that the last spring frost that year was on June the twenty-eighth and the first fall frost on July the first.

Summer precipitation is scant at Mile 1019. This was registered firmly when Cliff Stacey rashly counseled Abbott that the alfalfa field with growth three inches high, had been clipped too short.

"What do you mean, clipped? We haven't cut it at all!"

It was an experience for the scientists from Ottawa. Harry Gutteridge, poultry specialist, amassed a wealth of statistics on the economics of egg production at each stop but encountered brick-wall resistance at Mile 1022. Here, Mrs. MacIntosh, lodge-keeper with a Ph. D. degree in food management from Cornell, was adamant.

"Fresh eggs? I never use them. They lack substance!"

The same lady never forgave nor admitted Jack Abbott's naming of "her" mountain in honor of Dr. Archibald.

One night, the pastoral solitude of the visitors and Mrs. MacIntosh was blasted by some 600 "six by sixes," United States Army troops and equipment on military exercise, bedded down for the night in the open area near the lodge. The jarring cacophony of New York traffic could not have been worse in that pristine setting.

Contact was established between Beaverlodge and various agrologists in Alaska but it was not until the Station at Mile 1019 was under way that an interchange of visits was effected. In 1950 an invitation was extended to the superintendent at Beaverlodge to attend and present a paper at the September meeting of the Alaska Section of the American Association for the Advancement of Science, to be held at Mount McKinley National Park.

The visit to the Fairbanks Experiment Station and University of Alaska was exceedingly interesting and Stacey was beginning to realize he was indeed, in the North. Dr. Allan Mick of the Matanuska Experiment Station explained that there were some 5,000,000 acres in Alaska considered arable after permafrost was dissipated.

The procedure was interesting. First the thin layer of moss and vegetation was thrown into windrows about 200 feet apart. The next summer the intervening area would be lake-like from melting permafrost. Some five years later the permafrost would have disappeared from working depths and the moisture evaporated. Then the windrows would be spread out and farming commenced.

That summer a somewhat awkward situation had occurred on the University of Alaska campus when a crater-like cavity about an acre in size and twenty feet deep was caused by removal of the insulation layer and thus the withdrawal of the permafrost.

The meetings of the A.A.A.S had attracted numerous field parties en route "Stateside" and reports were heard on reindeer nutrition, Eskimo folklore, and defense problems. The Beaverlodge contribution was an analysis of cropping similarities and the advisability of close co-operation in research for mutual benefit.

Farther south at Matanuska, agriculture was observed in a different setting — maritime in summer and arctic in winter. Director Don Irvin, who had established the original Matanuska colonization settlement during the 1930's, was a delightful host.

Since then, Beaverlodge staff members have met frequently and profitably with Alaskan agrologists in friendly reciprocity.

THE CHALLENGE

D<small>R</small>. W. D. ALBRIGHT'S dream is becoming a reality. It had long been frustrating to hear Canadians, let alone Americans, refer to Edmonton's position as being in "northern" Canada while any school boy knew it was below the provincial center. Also, it was awkward to maintain composure when Beaverlodge — or the Peace River region, for that matter — was classified as "north," somewhat synonymous with "arctic." In little more than half a century the fur trade has given way to settlement, oxen to horses and horses to engine power, binders to combines, and trails to highways. The agricultural frontier has been pushed virtually to the Arctic Circle, the co-ordination of agricultural research in the Northwest Territories and the Yukon by Stacey and supported by Divisional Officers at Ottawa was a progressive step, as was the appointment of full-time co-ordinator, Frank Nowosad.

Finally, in 1965 the status of the Beaverlodge Experimental Station was changed to Research Station, with Dr. A. A. Guitard as Director. Initially the move encompassed the experimental farms at Fort Vermilion, Mile 1019 Alaska Highway, and Fort Simpson. The experimental farm at Prince George was brought into the family later that year, the family to be known as the Northern Research Group.

Dr. Guitard undertook to assess the extent and potentialities of the region to the Northwest Resources Conference held in Grande Prairie, May the twenty-ninth, 1969:

> Northwestern Canada is capable of producing large quantities of food. This capability forms a great resource which if properly developed and managed, will increase in value with use. It is located mainly in the watershed of the Peace River on what is essentially a fragmented northern extension of the Great Plains but the ability to produce cool season crops extends to the Arctic Ocean. It is expected that the development of these lands will not come about in a concen-

trated manner until nearly all of the land in the presently settled parts of the Peace River region has been developed for agriculture. It is then reasonable to assume that there will be tentacles of development northward along the Alaska Highway, the Mackenzie Highway and along certain of the river systems, creating a finger-like northward extension of the Peace River production system.

The soil and climate of the Peace River region are complex and variable. The variations are not strongly associated with latitude but rather with small local variations in topography. In climate there are also violent yearly fluctuations. However, underlying these variations are a number of soil and climatic characteristics that can be used to broadly describe the region. The soils are universally deficient in phosphorus and under continuous cropping are deficient in nitrogen. There are certain areas with sulphur deficiency and there are indications of regional deficiencies in boron and other micronutrients.

Mean precipitation ranges from slightly more than 17 inches at Beaverlodge in the southern part of the region to 12 inches at Fort Vermilion in the northern part. From one-half to two-thirds of the precipitation falls during the summer, with maximum rainfall during July. This favorable distribution of moisture, combined with lower evaporation than in the south, makes efficient moisture use possible but, nonetheless, the region is still deficient in moisture for maximum production. The average killing-frost-free period at Beaverlodge is 132 days and at Fort Vermilion 105 days. The growing season is somewhat longer in preferred river valley locations but there are numerous areas in which the growing season is less than 80 days. Generally, with progression northward, there is a shortening of the growing season but this is compensated for by increase in daylength.

On these soils, and subject to this climate, approximately 2,500,000 acres are now used annually for the production of wheat, oats, barley, flax and rapeseed. Some 800,000 acres are used for the production of forages for hay, pasture and seed and a further 700,000 acres are summerfallowed. Part of the grain and forage is used to feed less than 100,000 cattle, 150,000 hogs and a few sheep. A considerable quantity of grain is used within the region or moved from the region for seed. The remainder is moved from the region for feed and for processing.

With harvests ranging between 10,000,000 and 20,000,000 pounds, the region is producing virtually all of Canada's seed of creeping red fescue. It is also producing approximately 35 per cent of the bromegrass seed in Canada and has a few producers of timothy, bluegrass, Russian wild ryegrass, meadow fescue and crested wheatgrass.

In the legumes the region is producing annually 70 per cent of Canada's alsike clover seed, 50 per cent of the red clover, 40 per cent of the alfalfa and 20 per cent of the sweet clover.

Complimentary to the legume seed specialty is a rapidly expanding honey production industry, with output from approximately 50,000 colonies of bees. Finally, there is the nucleus of a small but diversified horticultural enterprise producing strawberries, potatoes, carrots, turnips, cucumbers, tomatoes, sweet corn and other staples.

This is an industry that has evolved during the past 55 years under essentially a homestead economy, an industry now producing a sufficiently broad spectrum of basic agricultural materials for moderate production stability. But also an industry that is highly vulnerable in that it is producing materials essentially for export in their basic form and is little involved directly with processing and merchandising.

We have considerable knowledge of the soils and climate of the areas that are now in production and rather broad estimates of the production potential of the areas that will be brought into production in the future. These indicate that the potential can be best expressed by the production of feed grains, and forage crops and the marketing of these through beef, cattle and hogs. Not more than 60 per cent of most of the soils should grow annual cereal and oilseed crops during a given year. A further 20 per cent should be used to produce pure stands of grasses or legumes or combinations of the two. Another 10 per cent is required for farmsteads, native treed areas that are not easily cultivated and planted field windbreaks to reduce wind velocity and evaporation. The final 10 per cent is required for summerfallowing, primarily after breaking out of forage stands, but also in certain select cases for intensive weed control.

With this production balance and using present varieties and production methods, each 1,000,000 acre production unit in the Peace River region is capable of producing annually 18,000,000 bushels of cereals and oilseeds, 17,000,000 pounds of grass and legume seed and 300,000 tons of forage stored as hay, silage or modifications of these. Of the 18,000,000 bushels of cereals and oilseeds some 10,000,000 bushels should be feed grain which in combination with the 300,000 tons of forage, can be best fed to 75,000 beef and dairy animals and 150,000 hogs. The beef industry will also use some 300,000 to 400,000 acres of rough land as pasture. Supplementary to this main production scheme, there should be on each 1,000,000 acre production unit, 15,000 colonies of bees to maximize legume seed production and these would produce annually 2,000,000 pounds of honey. And finally, there should be integrated with this a small horticultural enterprise to meet the demands of the some 130,000 people living in the region.

Based on present technology this is our estimate of the food production capability of 1,000,000 acres fully arable land in the Peace River region. Four such units are now developed and a further nine units are capable of being developed for agricultural production. There is associated with these another 13,000,000 acres that can be used for auxiliary pasture for livestock.

Dr. Guitard has presented a staggering but conservative appraisal of the potential of the Peace River region. The fulfillment of this production will be possible only with a corresponding increase in population and it would seem foolish in the light of world trends to deny that such will take place. In keeping, there will be the manufacturing and mercantile shift and development which will accompany it all. Increased freight rates and handling costs necessitate decentralization of industry.

Gone, too, will be the aura of the frontier of hardship and privation. History tells of tribulation in the backwoods of Ontario, on ranches in the southern Prairies, on wheat fields in soil-blowing areas. Eventually these difficulties were overcome. Much of the Peace is in midway position, some of it still struggling against the forces of Nature.

It may not be fanciful to hold that the North will find its increased population from those who appreciate, and insist on having, clean air to breathe and pure water to drink. Already there is concern that pollution and degradation in some older parts may already be beyond repair.

But why stop with the Peace? There is much land to the north and west which will fit the Guitard formula, with minor adjustment for climate and allowing more time for economic development and population build-up. Within a generation there has been a substantial development in mining, a development of hydroelectrical energy, and the discovery of major supplies of oil and natural gas. The pity is that all is being exported, some even to foreign lands, so that Canada and the North are not reaping the rewards of refinement and manufacture. Possibly the pittance received as revenue and wages will enhance greater development and the desire to retain a major economic portion.

Professor John Macoun is to be praised for his comprehensive report in 1873; he was, in effect, a one-man commission investigating a vast wilderness region. James Macoun's thoughts in 1903 have been echoed in terms of frozen crops and transportation costs, but no more than those experienced by the early settlers of the Red River Valley. No true pioneer has regretted his participation in developing the North nor the result of his endeavors. Should the good life be measured in terms of those who huddle in cities, where those who live a few blocks from a bus line are considered underprivileged? There are others who prefer to fend for themselves, to live in less settled regions, supported by a few amenities: adequate roads, electricity, and a shared telephone line.

Conservatively, the Beaverlodge staff estimates the present cultivated acreage:

Peace River region........................	3,500,000 acres
North-Central interior of B.C.......	100,000 acres

Potentially arable soils are another matter:

Peace River region:

Upper Peace River region............	7,500,000 acres
Lower Peace River region............	6,000,000 acres
North-Central interior, B.C..........	1,000,000 acres
Northern B.C.-Fort Nelson..........	500,000 acres

Yukon Territory:

Takhini and Dezadeash Valleys....	200,000 acres
Yukon River and tributaries	60,000 acres
Other	40,000 acres

Northwest Territories:

Slave River Lowland.....................	1,700,000 acres
Fort Providence and Mackenzie Valley..	1,400,000 acres
Liard Valley.................................	700,000 acres

Thus the total potential arable land for this region is estimated at 19,100,000 acres. When the cultivated acreage is added, the total farming area covers 22,700,000 acres. The present cultivated acreage in Western Canada, Manitoba through to British Columbia, is 87,000,000 acres.

Broken down, the potential arable land of the region is classified as:

Gray Wooded	13,500,000 acres
Meadow	2,500,000 acres
Brown Wooded	1,200,000 acres
Regosol (Undifferentiated)	600,000 acres
Other	1,300,000 acres

Further, it is estimated that in the Peace region there is fully an additional 13,000,000 acres of nonarable land which is well suited to summer grazing of cattle without conflicting with forestry or wild life. Possibly as much more exists in other regions of the North, though the amount is not known since the necessary surveys have yet to be made. Some would call this submarginal land. It is, indeed, in terms of grain production, but for grazing it is a valuable asset, as is the ranch land of the short-grass Prairies.

"The future of Canada lies in its breadth," said Donald Albright as he left Ontario to settle in the Peace. Today he would be amazed at the resources which have been found but would caution about undue haste in exploiting them. He would view *The North in the Eyes of the North.*

APPENDIX I

The original rental agreement between W. D. Albright and the Dominion of Canada on the establishment of the Dominion Experimental Sub-Station, as prepared by M. W. Eagar, of Grande Prairie, Alberta, in June, 1917, read:

"I, William D. Albright
of Beaverlodge in the Province of Alberta, Farmer,
hereinafter called the Lessor, being registered as owner of an estate in possession, subject, however, to such mortgages and encumbrances as are notified by memorandum underwritten or endorsed hereon of

THAT PIECE OF LAND known and described as follows: FIRSTLY all that portion of the South West Quarter of Section One (1), Township Seventy-two (72), Range Ten (10), West of Sixth Meridian, Containing by admeasurement Twenty-five (25) acres more or less, and more particularly described on the plan hereto attached. SECONDLY All that portion of the South East Quarter of Section One (1), Township Seventy-two (72), Range Ten (10), West of the Sixth Meridian, Containing by admeasurement Fifteen (15) acres more or less, and more particularly described on the plan hereto attached.

DO HEREBY LEASE to the Dominion of Canada, Department of Agriculture, hereinafter called the Lessee, all the said lands to be held by him the said The Dominion of Canada, Department of Agriculture as tenant for the space of five years from the First day of April 1920, at the yearly rental of Four Hundred dollars ($400.00) payable in even portions on the 31st day of March during the continuance of the said term:

THE next payment to be made on the 31st day of March, 1922, and powers implied and hereinafter expressed, subject to the covenants.

The Lessor reserves the right to the use of an implement shed situate on the premises herein and the property of the Lessor, for his own personal use as well as that of experimental purposes.

The lands herein are expressly leased to the Lessee for experimental purposes.

The contract ran from year to year, with an annual payment of $400.00 for land rental and an allowance of $75.00 for horse hire. In 1934, the allowance for horse hire was increased to $125.00.

The agreement was terminated in 1940 when the property was sold to the Crown.

APPENDIX II

The employees of the Beaverlodge Experimental Sub-Station to 1942, with approximate dates of service, include:

Paul Flint	1918-1930	F. J. Greer	
Albert Anderson	1919-1929	O. A. Black	
Anton Phillips	1920-1922	Willis Jeffcoat	1925
F. G. Hartwell		Murdo McLennan	1925-1926
D. Truax		John Taylor	1925
J. H. Bell		George Neely	1925-1927
K. L. Sinclair		W. A. Ross	1925-1928
R. E. Leake	1921	Bruce Perrin	1925
Robert Watson	1921-1927	Norman Perrin	1925
Gordon S. Moyer	1922-1924	Jeff Russell	1925
J. Walls		A. Brown	1926
George Baird	1922-1926	G. P. Gower	1926-1927
W. F. Baird	1923	A. McLennan	1926
J. W. Boyd	1923	E. S. Stockdale	1926
W. McLean	1923	J. Thiesson	1926-1928
J. Strong	1923	Sam Wright	1926-1928
Stanley Anderson		Kris Eidsmo	1927
W. J. Bell	1923	G. H. Tyrrell	1927-1929
H. Baring	1923	Adalar Gedeon	1927
A. Risbo	1923	W. E. Reynolds	1927
Gordon Greig	1923-1926	Miss Sadie Hommy	1927
Tom Russell	1923-1924	Art Tyrrell	1927
E. J. Heller	1923-1924	John Foster	1927-1942
W. Greig	1923-1924	J. E. Nickel	1927
Daws Johnson	1924-1928	J. M. Skelton	1928
G. P. Anderson	1924-1925	R. M. Odlum	1928-1931
E. C. Stacey	1924-1962	Victor Thiel	1928-1935
W. C. Stephens	1924-1926	K. Bell	1928
D. C. Hume	1924-1925	Miss Ruth C. Stone	1928
R. H. Elliott		Miss B. M. Wilson	1928
Don McLennan			
C. Greer			
O. Wright			

Miss Violet J.
Fielding........... 1928-1929
E. P. Davis......... 1928
R. E. Campbell.. 1928-1934
Harry Bruels...... 1928
John Snider........ 1928
Douglas Skelton 1928
W. V. Harcourt 1928-1930
Miss M. Roberts 1928-1935
Miss O. E.
Kolosoff.......... 1929-1933
Vladimir P.
Ignatieff.......... 1929-1930
Gordon Fawkes.. 1929-1933
Ivan Fawkes........ 1929
Cecil Fawkes...... 1929-1939
Miss H.
McCullough ....
Calvin Snider......
A. E. Carlson..... 1930-1931
John Cussack...... 1930-1936
L. M. Godfrey ... 1930-1935
F. B. Albright.... 1930-1940
C. E. Gardiner... 1930
I. C. Shank........ 1930
J. H. Crossley.... 1931-1934
J. E. Crawford.... 1932-1934
Bruce Holmwood 1933
John Butler........
S. W. Harris...... 1934
J. B. Harcourt.... 1934-1936
A. H. Abbott..... 1934-1938
N. C. Ehlinger... 1934
J. J. Haan........... 1934
M. R. Worden ... 1934
R. F. Gibson...... 1935-1936
A. B. Dixon....... 1935-1941
Lawrence Oszust 1925-1936

J. G. Stoker....... 1935
Cornelius Fast 1935
H. E. Stringer.... 1935
A. C. Carder...... 1935
Peter Neufeld 1936
John Walli.......... 1936-1937
Hugh Allison...... 1936
A. H. Saunders.. 1936-1937
T. H. Martin...... 1936
J. Peterson.......... 1936
T. R. Smith........ 1937-1938
L. D. Fraser 1937-1943
J. F. Moore........ 1937-1942
E. W. Caulson.... 1937
L. R. Emes......... 1938-1963
E. H. Jeffrey...... 1938
Albert Parry........ 1938-1942
C. H. Anderson
Albert Clease 1939
Hans Waelti 1939-1941
Mervyn Jaque..... 1939-1941
A. J. Clease........ 1940
D. A. Elliott....... 1940
R. G. Albright ... 1940-1942
O. P. Hegland ... 1941
T. F. Rowell....... 1941-1942
Miss F. A.
L'Hirondelle..... 1941-1943
Philip Purvis....... 1942
Peter
L'Hirondelle.... 1942
Cliff Hegland 1942
D. J. Nickel....... 1942
Allan
MacKimmie 1942
P. J. Enns........... 1942
Miss M. C.
MacDonald 1942

APPENDIX III

The pay-list of the Beaverlodge Experimental Sub-Station, June 1-15, 1937, bears the following record:

Year Round Employee	Labourer	Rate of Wages	Net Amount of Wages
A. H. Abbott......	,,	27½ hrs. at 32c per hr.	$ 8.80
Fast, C.................	,,	91 hrs. at 28c per hr.	25.48
Foster, J.	,,	110 hrs. at 26c per hr.	28.60
Gibson, R. F.......	,,	100 hrs. at 55c per hr.	55.60
Moore, John F....	,,	108 hrs. at 35c per hr.	57.80
Stoker, J. G........	,,	125½ hrs at 30c per hr.	37.65
Casual Employees			
Allison, H.	,,	64 hrs. at 25c per hr.	16.00
Carder A. C........	,,	105 hrs. at 28c per hr.	29.40
Fraser, Leon.......	,,	106½ hrs. at 30c per hr.	31.95
Neufeld, P.	,,	34 hrs. at 25c per hr.	5.50
Saunders, A.........	,,	60 hrs. at 25c per hr.	15.00
Smith, T..............	,,	72½ hrs. at 25c per hr.	18.13

The Classified Staff was recorded September 10, 1941, as follows:

Name	Position	Degrees	Remarks
W. D. Albright	Superintendent		
E. C. Stacey	Assistant, Gr. 2	B.A., M.Sc., Alta.	Assistant (agronomy)
A. C. Carder	Agrl. Asst. (8)	B.S.A.-U. of B.C. Post-graduate work U. of A. and Macdonald College	In charge, under Stacey of field husbandry and forage crop work
J. F. Moore	Asst., Gr. 1	B.Sc. Alberta M.Sc.	Asst. in charge of horticulture and apiculture
L. D. Fraser	Asst. Agrl. (7)	B.Sc. Alberta	In charge of animal husbandry & illustration station work
C.H. Anderson	Asst. Agrl. (5)	B.Sc. Alberta	In charge under Stacey & Carder
J. G. Stoker	Plotman		Functions as foreman and reads weather records.

On September 30, 1943, the Director's office recorded that Superintendent Albright had been in service 28 years, 6 months, and his salary currently was $2,520 plus cost-of-living bonus of $78.12.

APPENDIX IV

The first boarding house for the staff was a log building bought from Daws Johnson, of Beaverlodge. Over the years it and its replacements have been in charge of Mrs. Gillespie, Mrs. A. A. Black, Mrs. William Greig, Mrs. Charles Stephens, Mrs. D. C. Hume, Mrs. Gordon Fawkes, Mrs. Lem Wilder, Mrs. A. H. Abbott, Mrs. Hazel Elliott, Mrs. R. E. Campbell, Mrs. Art Schaffter, Mrs. L. Johnson, Mrs. George Miller, Mrs. Art Walker, and Mrs. Ed Batter.

APPENDIX V

Expenses of E. C. Stacey for period ending June 23, 1939, attending field days at Debolt, Rycroft, North Star, and Strong Creek, Alta., in co-operation with the Alberta Department of Agriculture, and miscellaneous mileage in connection with field studies of red-backed cutworms.

June 19	Lunch, 40c, supper 50c, Grande Prairie, Alta.	.90
20	Room, Grande Prairie, Alberta	1.50
	Breakfast, Grande Prairie	.35
	Lunch, 45c; dinner 45c, Rycroft, Alta.	.90
21	Room, Berwyn, Alta.	1.50
	Breakfast, Berwyn, Alta.	.50
	Lunch, North Star, Alta.	.40
	22 Room, Peace River, Alta.	1.50
	Dinner, Peace River, Alta.	.45
	Breakfast, Peace River, Alta.	.25
	Lunch, Berwyn, Alta.	.45
	Dinner, Peace River, Alta.	.50
23	Room, McLennan, Alta.	1.50
	Breakfast, McLennan, Alta.	.30
	Ticket, N.A.R., McLennan to Grande Prairie	4.20
	Dinner, Grande Prairie, Alta.	.40
	Mileage, per A101A Mileage Diary—	
	180 miles at 9c	16.20
		31.80

APPENDIX VI

The W. D. Albright Scholarship Committee was composed of:

C. H. Anderson, Beaverlodge
V. C. Flint, Beaverlodge
E. C. Stacey, Beaverlodge
G. S. Moyer, Elmworth
R. S. MacMillan, Grande Prairie
H. W. Allen, Huallen
L. F. Stickney, Hythe
L. C. Howard, Sexsmith

The following received awards:

1946-47	Douglas Mackie, Beaverlodge
1947-48	Merle Summers, Crooked Creek
1952-53	Ted Plante, Peace River
	Dorothy Langer, Three Creeks
1954-55	A. M. Mollevost, Peace River
1956-57	Robert Gustafson, High Prairie
	James Backer, Sexsmith
1957-58	Mary Supernault, Paddle Prairie
1964-65	Fred White, Beaverlodge
	Harold Bratland, Hythe
	Sharon Befus, Peace River
1965-66	Karen Pool, Beaverlodge
	Jeannette Boisvert, Girouxville
	Dale Sather, Wanham
1966-67	Larry Southwell, Goodfare
	Carol Schamehorne, Notikewin
	Joyce Bulhofner, Northmark
1967-68	Sheila Burgeson, Hines Creek
	Glen Snelgrove, Fairview
1968-69	Margo Hindmarch, Blueberry Mountain
	Vivian Rey, Falher
1969-70	Annie Hayday, High Level
	Tom Medynski, High Level
1970-71	Marvin Stefan, Wembley

APPENDIX VII

Since the establishment of the Northern Research Group, Dr. Guitard has been transferred to the Research Station at Swift Current, Saskatchewan, as Director.

His successor, Dr. Lloyd P. S. Spangelo, a native of Manitoba, has achieved scientific fame as a pomologist and was a valuable member of the Ottawa Research Station. He came to Beaverlodge Research Station well-equipped as its new director.

Working with Dr. Spangelo on his professional staff are the following:

ADMINISTRATION
M. D. Hamilton......................................Administrative Officer
J. A. Reilly, C.D....................................Office Manager

CEREAL CROPS
D. G. Faris, B.S.A., M.S.A., Ph.D.........Head: Oilseed Crops;
Utility Wheat

ENVIRONMENT AND SPECIAL CROPS
R. E. Harris, B.S.A., M.S.A., Ph.D. ......Head
A. L. Darwent, B.S.A., M.Sc., Ph.D.....Weed Control
J. G. N. Davidson, B.S.F., M.Sc., Ph.D. Plant Pathology
J. S. McKenzie, B.Sc., M.Sc., Ph.D. ......Plant Survival

FORAGE CROPS
P. Pankiw, B.S.A., M.Sc., Ph.D..............Head
S. G. Bonin, B.S.A., Ph.D......................Grass Breeding
C. R. Elliott, B.Sc., M.Sc., Ph.D............Grass Seed Production
D. L. Nelson, B.S.A., M.Sc....................Apiculture
W. L. Pringle, B.S.A., M.S.F..................Utilization

SOILS
P. B. Hoyt, B.S.A., M.S., Ph.D............Head
A. M. F. Hennig, B.Sc...........................Management
W. A. Rice, B.S.A., M.Sc., Ph.D..........Microbiology
R. Leitch, B.Sc. (Agr)., B.Sc.
(Chem), M.Sc. ....Soil Fertility

EXPERIMENTAL FARM, FORT VERMILION, ALBERTA
B. Siemens, B.S.A., M.Sc.......................Superintendent

EXPERIMENTAL FARM, PRINCE GEORGE, B.C.
W. K. Dawley, B.Sc. ....Superintendent;
Forage Utilization
J. N. Tingle, B.Sc., M.Sc........................Forage Management

APPENDIX VIII

Recognition should also be given to a few unheralded horticulturists of Western Canada who have made distinct contributions to better living in the North and who have shared their genetic thoughts with the Beaverlodge staff.

Percy H. Wright

Percy H. Wright was a nurseryman at Moose Range, Saskatchewan, but after being flooded out several times, turned to journalism and teaching. Always a horticulturist, he is still breeding for better quality shrub roses and hardy lilies.

His most popular rose is Ruth, developed from the Apothecaries French rose. It is hardy, vigorous and under favorable moisture conditions, produces a good crop of double rose-red bloom.

Hazeldean is an excellent yellow-blossomed variety, a shade deeper than Harrison's Yellow and hardy. Robert Simonet rates Hazeldean higher than Persian Yellow and Harrison's Yellow.

The Red Knight strain of dark red Turkscap lilies was developed in his nursery days and Wright is now working with apparent success with daylilies, apples, and plums. He is particularly interested in his cherry-plum Wessex. Unfortunately it may be too late for northern districts.

A. J. Porter

A. J. Porter lives at Parkside, Saskatchewan, and is known far and wide for his improved varieties of strawberries Sparta, Northerner, Jubilee, and Parkland, to name the most outstanding.

Jubilee is an everbearer and one of the most satisfactory varieties offered to home gardeners in Western Canada.

Parkside gooseberry is another Porter valuable contribution. It is hardy and the largest-fruited variety adapted to this climate.

Still another contribution is the Willoughby black currant, obtained as a seedling from a neighbor and quickly recognized for its resistance to mildew.

Porter's lilies include Earlibird, Rusty, Rosabelle, and more recently, Firebright and Redland. His Red Knight lilies were developed from seed produced by Dr. Richard Palmer of the Summerland Research Station from crosses made between Percy Wright's dark selections and his own material. Robert Simonet of Edmonton originated the Black Butterfly lily but Porter introduced it. This lily won an Award of Commendation at the International Lily Show of the North American Lily Society in 1966.

Bert Porter has discontinued his raspberry and strawberry breeding and is now working with hardy plums and lilies. Morden and Saskatoon have dropped all breeding work with plums, leaving Porter to carry the banner for this valuable species.

In 1964 Mr. Porter received the Stevenson Memorial Gold Medal, one of North America's most prized horticultural awards.

Georges Bugnet

Georges Bugnet was born in Burgundy, February 1879. Mr. and Mrs. Bugnet came to Canada from France in 1905, lured by immigration literature. Educated at Sorbonne and Lyons University, it was no wonder that in the quiet of the winter months he turned to writing. Six novels resulted, the best known being *Nipsya*. He also wrote a book of poems and a number of essays.

But Georges Bugnet is better known for his improvement of ornamentals.

While at Lake Majeau he secured from Petrograd, just before the Russian revolution of 1917, seed of the Kamchatka rose which grows in extreme northeast Siberia. He crossbred it with the Canadian wild rose, and further developed it by crossbreeding with other roses, including the Japanese double rose. From this hybridization and 25 years' work, came the famed, almost thornless Thérèse Bugnet, a durable, fragrant double rose which blooms from mid-June until freeze-up. It is one of the most popular varieties in Western Canada and is rated highly in California as well as in New York. It has invaded at least three countries in Europe.

Other roses are: Lac La Nonne, Marie Bugnet, Betty Bugnet, Louise Bugnet, Rita Bugnet, and Lac Majeau, the latter a pillar rose with a height of 12 feet in favored locations.

Outstanding on his farm was a stately line of Scots pine. His Ladoga strain is more vigorous than most hardy strains and carries its green needles throughout the winter.

In the garden is the sweetberry honeysuckle, varieties Georges Bugnet and Julia Bugnet, edible-fruited selections akin to the native blueberry; also the Claude Bugnet, a hybrid of sandcherry and Manitoba plum.

When Superintendent Stacey and horticulturist John Wallace visited the Bugnets at Lake Majeau in 1948, they were charmed by the genuine hospitality and graciousness of their hosts. They were equally impressed how simply life can be enriched. A sod patch is plowed or a few trees removed, the hybrid seed planted and the seedlings left to survive the vicissitudes of Nature and await the search of a genius. A little luck, much perseverance and 25 years' work and the result is a Thérèse Bugnet to be shared by thousands. Growth chambers were not in the picture.

Robert Simonet

Robert Simonet lives three miles east of Edmonton on Highway 14. Originally a market gardener, he conferred with Prof. J. S. Shoemaker and later with Prof. R. J. Hilton at the University of Alberta, who pronounced him the most thoroughly grounded, uneducated geneticist ever known and one of the most modest.

During World War II he supplied the North American market with seed of double petunias, as the Japanese trade was cut off. Since then, he was developed many fine varieties listed in seed catalogues. His Powder Puff hollyhocks are currently going well. He has also produced a number of varieties of gladioli and now directs his attention to lily hybridization. He regards Thérèse Bugnet as Georges Bugnet's best rose variety but is even more interested in two seedlings he received from Bugnet. These commenced to flower when only three inches high and are true everbloomers. Obviously he is using them in his breeding program.

Possibly the most spectacular Simonet achievement is a saskatoon-mountain ash hybrid, with berries closer to the saskatoon than the mountain ash. Seedlings from this hybrid vary widely in form and show very wide differences in growth and vigor. Some have foliage closer to mountain ash but with red berries, some of which are quite mild-flavored. Others have undivided leaves and some produce berries larger than saskatoons. Six generations of selections have resulted in considerable improvement in plant and berry qualities and the work is proceeding.

Simonet's present interest, other than the petunias, is to produce hardier hybrid tea roses, also earlier perennial asters, hardier red coral-bells, and better lilies. After some years he is securing promising results with everbearing strawberries.

In his market garden days he developed improved varieties of cabbage, garden peas, turnip, parsnip, sweet corn, and rhubarb.

In 1960 Robert Simonet received the Stevenson Memorial Gold Medal, thus ranking with Bert Porter.

★ ★ ★

The highest praise which can be given this wonderful group of horticulturists is that they maintain a very warm and close fraternity. No doubt this serves to spark them on to greater achievement and may carry them over times of disappointment. All but one finance plant breeding by other means — commercial nurseries, writing, etc., and all will welcome the passing of plant patent legislation to give them greater funds for exploring and hybridization.

An illustration of this fraternity: The Western Canada Society for Horticulture asked John Wallace to present to Georges Bugnet its Honorary Membership award at the annual meeting held at Banff in 1967. This was a great honor to Bugnet and for Wallace.

Then to his surprise, Wallace was requested to remain on stage while he in turn was presented with his Award of Merit by the Society for his introduction of the Dunvegan blue juniper.

Index[1]

Abbott, A. H., 166
Abbott, Mrs. A. H., 167
Abbott, Jack, 128, 134, 135, 138, 151, 152, 153, 154, 155
Abbott's Illustration Station, 37, 40
Acadia Valley, Alta., 91
Ackland farm, 153
Adam, Rev. viii
Adanac Hotel, Falher, 98
Agricultural Institute of Canada, 88
ARDA, 74, 76, 138
Aitchison, Jock, viii
Aklavik, N.W.T., 39, 43, 145, 146, 147, 149
Alaska, 35, 62, 120, 128, 150, 151, 156
Alaska Highway, 62, 128, 135, 151, 154, 155, 158
Alberta, x, 2, 11, 13, 30, 54, 60, 73, 85, 92, 107, 110, 112, 118, 130, 149, 163
Alberta Agricultural Institute, Peace River Branch, 140
Alberta Department of Agriculture, 85, 102, 109, 118, 138, 142, 167
AIA-BCIA (Albert-British Columbia Institute of Agrologists), 140
Alberta Master Beekeepers' Awards, 85
Alberta Parliamentary Library, vi
Alberta Research Council, 71, 75
Alberta soil testing laboratory, 78
Albright, Bruce, 15
Albright, Eileen (Mrs. Wm. Ross), 15, 38
Albright, Gordon, 15, 53
Albright, Josiah D., 14
Albright, Sarah Elizabeth, 14
Albright, Mrs. W. D., 9, 14, 15, 52, see also Lossing, Eva
Albright cairn, viii, 52, 53
Albright, W. D. Scholarship awards, see Appendix VI, 168
Albright, W. D. Scholarship Committee, see Appendix VI, 168
Albright, W. D. Scholarship Fund, 57
alfalfa, viii, 80, 83, 84, 86, 88, 89, 97, 108, 135, 159
Allen, H. W., 34, 168
Allison, H., 166
alsike clover, 84, 88, 90, 97, 108, 159
Altaswede red clover, 88, 90

American Association for the Advancement of Science, 156
American Peony Society, 130
Anderson, Albert, 61
Anderson, Andrew, 91
Anderson, C. Henry, 63, 76, 80, 115, 143, 166, 168
Anderson, Ken, 68
Annals of Horticulture, 131
Annapolis Valley, Nova Scotia, 126
apples, 125, 126, 127
apricots, 127
Archibald, Dr. E. S., 11, 63, 64, 142, 145, 155
Arctic Red River, 149
Ardill, Jack, 86
Arnold Arboretum, 62
Arnott, David A., 98
Athabaska, 5, 90
Athabasca ferry, vii
Athabaska River region, 30, 56
Athabaska River watershed, 134
Aurora clover, 90
Austria, 94

Baird, Bill, 26, 27
Baird, George, 26
Baird, Reg, 26
Baird, Sidney, 26
Baldonnel Illustration Station, B.C., 40, 134, 151
Balkan Alps, 91
Baring, H., 26
Barnum, P. T., 114, 115
Barr Colonists, 2
Barrhead, Alta., 131
Batter, Mrs. Ed, 167
Battle River district, 138
Bauman, Jim, 27, 97
Beamsville, Ont., 14
Bear Lake, 68, 125
Bear Mountain, 75
Beatty, Sir Edward, 35
Beaver alfalfa, 89
Beaverlodge, Alta., vii, viii, 5, 21, 26, 43, 50, 51, 52, 53, 61, 62, 66, 69, 70, 71, 72, 98, 126, 150, 153, 157, 158, 163
Beaverlodge Industrial Co. Ltd., vii
Beaverlodge River, 5, 75
Beaverlodge valley, 5, 97
Beaverlodge's Victory Hall, 100
Beaverskin, Billy, 147
Belanger, A. B., 43, 137
Belleville, Ont., 67
Bennett, H. H., 45
Bennett, W. A. C., 62, 149
Bentley, Dean Fred, 74

---

[1]"W. D. Albright," "E. C. Stacey," "Beaverlodge Sub-Station" and "Research Station" and "Peace River Country," and/or "Region" appear with such frequency that separate entries have not been listed for them.

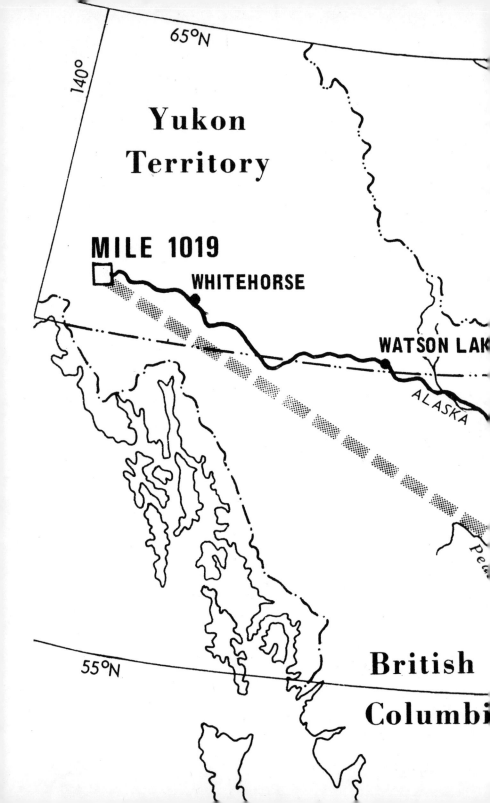